# AIR
# TRAFFIC
# CONTROL

# AIR TRAFFIC CONTROL

## DAVID ADAIR

 **Patrick Stephens, Wellingborough**

**Cover photographs:**
**Front** *An en-route sector suite in the operations room of the London Air Traffic Control Centre at West Drayton* (Civil Aviation Authority).
**Back** *The new stalk-mounted visual control room at Gatwick airport* (Civil Aviation Authority).

©David Adair 1985

First published in 1985

*British Library Cataloguing in Publication Data*

Adair, David
   Air traffic control.
   1. Air traffic control
   I. Title
   629.136'6       TL725.3.T7

   ISBN 0-85059-694-7

*Patrick Stephens Limited is part of the Thorsons Publishing Group, Wellingborough, Northamptonshire, NN8 2RQ, England.*

Printed in Great Britain by Adlard and Son Limited, The Garden City Press, Letchworth, Hertfordshire

10  9  8  7  6  5  4  3  2

# Contents

# Acknowledgements

No one individual can hope to have the breadth of knowledge necessary to write a book of this kind without recourse to external assistance. Air Traffic Control is a vast and complicated subject and is becoming more so as the introduction of more and more technology makes itself felt. It follows then that part of the research process consists of asking questions of colleagues as well as studying the written data already available. My general and grateful thanks go to those colleagues for putting up with my sudden appearances and equally unexpected questions. My particular thanks must go to Captain Michael Edwards of the Civil Aviation Authority Flying Unit, firstly for introducing me to the publishers, and secondly, but of no lesser importance, for encouraging me with good humour when it seemed as if the task was beyond completion. My particular thanks go also to Miss Katherine Bebbington of Poole for her patience and skill in turning my snapshots into presentable photographs.

I am also indebted to the McDonnell Douglas Corporation, Saint Louis, Missouri, USA, for providing data on aircraft development, and to the Boeing Commercial Airplane Company, Seattle, Washington, USA, for providing some superb cockpit photographs included in this book.

Finally it would be remiss of me not to express my thanks to the United Kingdom Civil Aviation Authority for agreeing to this project in the first instance and for their continued assistance thereafter.

Additional acknowledgements appear individually.

# Author's note

When I was first approached as a possible author for this book I was at once flattered and not a little hesitant. My direct association with aviation goes back to 1950 when, as an Air Training Corps Cadet for five years, I was fortunate to be able to fly in many of the older wartime aircraft. Then followed regular service in the Royal Air Force and, after a break of two years, a return to aviation when I entered the world of Air Traffic Control. I would lay legitimate claim to being an aviation enthusiast and knew just enough about ATC to appreciate that the writing of this book was going to be no simple task.

The book I have tried *not* to write is one full of minute technicalities or a condensed version of the many volumes of rules and regulations with which ATC abounds. It is written with the interested layman in mind, hopefully both to inform and entertain. If this book fires the imagination then other books are available for closer technical study. I have tried to impart some of the atmosphere that surrounds the operation of the ATC system and to give some insight into the human factors involved because, the influx of high technology not withstanding, it is still heavily reliant upon the skill of the individual.

This book is largely based upon factual information, such comment and opinion as it does contain is mine alone and is in no way intended to reflect or represent the views, policies or opinions of the United Kingdom Civil Aviation Authority.

*David Adair*
*Ringwood, December 1984*

# *Introduction*

At 10:04 hours GMT on September 10 1976 a British Airways Trident 3, registration *G–AWZT* and using the radio callsign BE 476, checked overhead a radio beacon at Klagenfurt in level flight at 33,000 ft. The aircraft had previously left London (Heathrow) and was on its way to Istanbul with 54 passengers and nine crew aboard. It was travelling along an upper air route designated as Upper Blue 5 which would take it to the next reporting point overhead the Zagreb radio beacon.

Some time prior to this an Inex-Adria DC 9, registration *YU-AJR* and using the radio callsign JP550, had departed the airfield at Split on its way to Cologne with 108 passengers and seven crew. This aircraft was climbing as cleared by Air Traffic Control to 26,000 ft. One minute after the Trident had checked overhead Klagenfurt, the DC 9 reported that it was levelling off at 26,000 ft and requested a further climb to a higher altitude. At 10:06 hours the DC 9 was advised that the levels at 28, 31 and 33,000 ft were not available, being occupied by other traffic, and was asked if a climb to 35,000 ft was acceptable. This was a perfectly normal procedure as some aircraft, at an early stage in their flight profile, cannot climb above a certain level until their weight has been reduced by burning off fuel. However, the climb was accepted and at 10:08 hours the DC 9 began to climb once more towards the upper air route designated as Upper Blue 9. This route also passed over the radio beacon at Zagreb. At 10:10 hours it passed 31,000 ft and, still climbing, was now rapidly approaching the Zagreb beacon. At 10:14 hours the Trident checked overhead the Zagreb beacon, level at 33,000 ft.

Six and a quarter miles below, in the darkened radar room of the Zagreb Air Traffic Control Centre, the awful truth dawned. The controller transmitted an urgent request to the DC 9 to ascertain its present height. The answer received was 32,500 ft and still climbing, and the tell-tale blips on the radar screen merged together, flared briefly, and were gone.

The Trident travelling in a south easterly direction had collided with the DC 9 travelling in a direction to the west of north. The port wing of the DC 9 struck the Trident at cockpit window level and smashed on through the fuselage. Both aircraft disintegrated and fell to earth. The combined speed at the moment of impact was over 1,000 mph and the disaster took 178 lives.

Subsequent investigation showed that the accident was wholly attributable to Air Traffic Control although the exact sequence of events leading up to the collision is still being questioned. A vital piece of co-odination between the Upper Sector controller who was looking after the Trident and the Middle Sector controller who was looking after the climbing DC 9 had either not taken place or the portent of the exchange of information had not been fully appreciated. Either way it made no difference to the final outcome.

Six months later, in March 1977, another misunderstanding, or more accurately, a series of misunderstandings, was to lead to an even more horrific accident. This time the setting was the holiday island of Tenerife and its airport at Los Rodeas. A bomb scare at Las Palmas, Canary Island, had caused a lot of extra traffic to divert to Tenerife. The weather here was very bad with low cloud crossing the airfield and reducing the visibility to a quarter of a mile or less. The airfield itself was badly congested with parked aircraft, so much so that it was not possible to taxy to the take-off point without first entering the runway against the direction of take-off. Aircraft then moved along the runway for some distance before clearing to the left preparatory to turning back on and lining up for their own take-off.

The first aircraft to appear on stage in this tragedy was a Boeing 747 belonging to the Dutch airline KLM, radio callsign KL4805. This aircraft was cleared to enter the main runway and to backtrack the full length to the take-off point. At this time that was all it was cleared to do. The second aircraft involved was also a Boeing 747 belonging to Pan American Airways and using the radio callsign Clipper 1736. This aircraft too was cleared on to the main runway to follow the KLM and then to turn off at the third turning to the left, thus allowing clear passage for the KLM to take off when it was cleared to go. Three nationalities were now involved and although English is the international language of aviation two of the three parties concerned were now listening and conversing in a foreign language. The tower controller, whose native tongue was Spanish, could see neither aircraft from his position because of the very poor visibility. There now occurred some confusion amongst the crew of the Pan American Clipper as to whether the turning they were looking for was the first or third to the left. The tower controller confirmed that it was the third. The KLM aircraft had, meanwhile, received its en-route clearance and had reported that it was at the take-off point, but it had still not been cleared to go. Transcripts of the voice recordings made on the flight deck of the KLM aircraft also indicate considerable confusion about their exact status within the ATC procedures. Believing that they were cleared to go, the power was applied and the huge aircraft began to accelerate along the runway. Meanwhile the Clipper was still moving slowly along the same runway and having some difficulty in locating the third turning off to the left. Out of the gloom the lights of the departing KLM were seen fast approaching and for nine long seconds the Clipper crew made a desperate effort to get their aircraft out of the way, but their efforts were to be in vain.

The departing KLM made an equally desperate attempt to become airborne but was trapped in that potentially dangerous phase which occurs during every take-off. Travelling too fast to stop and not yet fast enough to fly, they had no option left to them. The resultant appalling collision and subsequent fire was to take the lives of 583 people.

How could such disasters as those recounted here actually happen? How, with all the modern equipment, radars, computers and lengthy personnel training could the system break down with such hideous results? Perhaps the question should really be posed the other way around; why do they not happen more often?

**Chapter 1**

# *Aviation comes of age*

Tragic though such accidents are it must be remembered that whilst these dramas were being enacted, all around the world thousands of flights were arriving, departing, and transitting the world's air routes without the slightest danger to anyone. To the man on the ground the sky appears to be a huge and empty place but, in practice, this is not really so.

Lay writers and reporters when referring to aviation matters are fond of using analogy to try and bring understanding to the equally lay reader and viewer. Unfortunately the terminology used often only serves to confuse rather than clarify. Air Traffic Controllers are continually referred to as the men who 'talk down the aircraft' and every square foot of concrete at an airport is labelled as a runway. If all those aircraft need to be 'talked down' presumably someone put them all up there in the first place—guess who?

An oft quoted analogy compares the movement of aircraft within the airways system to the movement of trains within the rail network. True, both systems transport large numbers of people and quantities of freight over fixed routes between set points. But, supposing all of the trains going to say Manchester or Birmingham had to use just a single platform, not only for arrivals but also departures? It needs little imagination to envisage the chaos that would quickly ensue and yet this, in terms of the analogy, is what happens at an airport with only a single runway. Only one aircraft can use the concrete at one time and during busy periods this causes congestion and delay further back down the line. Furthermore, the disparity of traffic types is far greater in the airways system than on the railways.

Within the rules and regulations the sky belongs to all who wish to use it for both civil and military flying. At one end of the scale are the hot air balloons, hang gliders and micro-light aircraft, at the

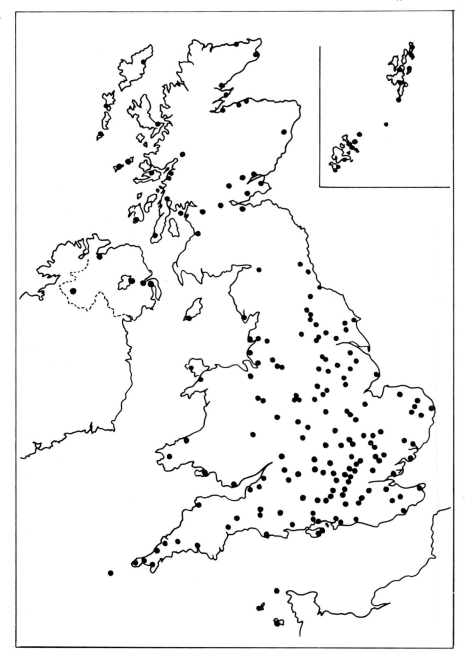

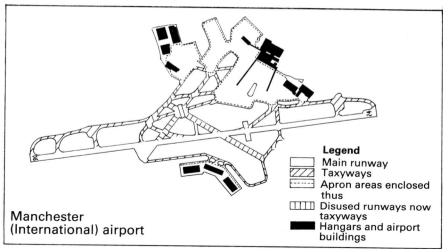

Manchester
(International) airport

**Legend**
☐ Main runway
▨ Taxyways
⋯ Apron areas enclosed thus
⊞ Disused runways now taxyways
▬ Hangars and airport buildings

**Above** *Parts of an airfield correctly identified.* (Produced from information supplied by the CAA.)

**Left** *The disposition of the main civil and military airfields and helicopter landing sites in the United Kingdom.* (Produced from information supplied by the CAA.)

other are the large civil transports such as the Boeing 747, DC 10, and Tristar. Concorde might fly well above its more mundane ancestors but it still has to share the same airspace at the beginning and end of its flight. Mix in private and business aircraft, helicopters, and all the requirements and demands made upon the system by the military fliers and it is not difficult to appreciate that an ATC system has to be both complex and flexible. Safety and the needs of the user are of paramount importance—however the combining of all these requirements and demands does not always make for an easy marriage.

In the following pages it is intended to describe the ATC system as it exists today, to look briefly at its development, and to look towards the way the system might develop in the future. In broad terms the ATC system is standardised throughout the world although nations do tend to impose their own variations on the basic structure. Further change in the method of application may also have to be made to provide a satisfactory service where, for instance, flights take place over large expanses of water or sparsely populated land masses.

On December 17 1903, when the Wright brothers undertook the

very first controlled powered flight of a heavier than air machine, those men of vision had seen a dream come true. Far sighted they might have been but they would have needed a prodigious imagination indeed to accept that in just 65 years that flight could have been comfortably accommodated within the fuselage length of a Lockheed 'Galaxy'. The total length of that first flight was 120 ft and the take-off weight of their frail machine was about 750 lb. By comparison the length of a 'Galaxy' is a fraction over 230 ft and its maximum take-off weight is 800,000 lb.

When the idea of powered manned flight became a reality the need for any form of control of the traffic which might be generated could not have been foreseen. The sky was a very big and empty place. For quite some time the evolution of the flying machine was to be a long drawn out process. Designers, engineers, and pilots (and very often they were one and the same person) slowly learned to master the new art. Gradually though, the lessons were learned, sometimes the hard way, and by 1909 designs had become reliable enough for Bleriot to cross the English Channel. Before too long there grew an air of euphoria and the flying machine was to become fashionable. The popular press of the day forecast 'aviation for everyman', a forecast which thankfully has not come true, at least not in the context in which it was originally made.

The war of 1914–1918 was to give the development of the aircraft, and in particular its power plant, a big boost so that at the end of hostilities aviation had become a reliable method of transport. Paradoxically it also fell out of popularity with the public. Nations had fought a terrible war of attrition and the aircraft, like so many of man's inventions, had become just one more way of dealing out death and destruction. Nevertheless development work went on and public enthusiasm was to be rekindled by the great pioneering flights. The Empire beckoned and there were many ready to set out on airborne adventures, to explore the world again but this time from a position well above its surface.

It is interesting to note at this point how much of the terminology used in aviation has come directly from the sea and the mariner. The aircraft commander became the captain, his flying companions became his crew, left and right were port and starboard. Other similarities were evident too. The sea captain was master of his vessel once at sea and solely responsible for the conduct of his voyage, his crew, and for the safety and comfort of his passengers. Likewise the captain of an airliner leaving Croydon for some far off destination such as India took unto himself the same responsibilities. Once aloft he was expected to meet and solve all problems that might come his way from the avoidance of bad weather to dealing with over inquisitive tribesmen. Aviation was no longer a newly born infant but had grown into a boisterous youngster. The sky though remained hardly disturbed by the passing traffic, the need for an air traffic control system was still some way off, and by and large the sky was still a big and empty place.

For much of the period just covered aviation was limited in its application both in terms of availability and feasibility. The old saying 'only fools and birds fly—and birds don't fly at night' had more than a grain of truth in it. The early aviators mostly waited for good weather, seldom flew at night and were restricted in any case by a lack of suitable equipment. For many years only three aids to navigation existed, the map, the magnetic compass, and what our American cousins refer to as 'the Mark 1 eyeball'. Excellent items all in suitable conditions, they were of very limited use in bad weather or at night.

The outbreak of war in 1939 was to accelerate events at an

*Examples of ground signals.* (Produced from information supplied by the CAA.)

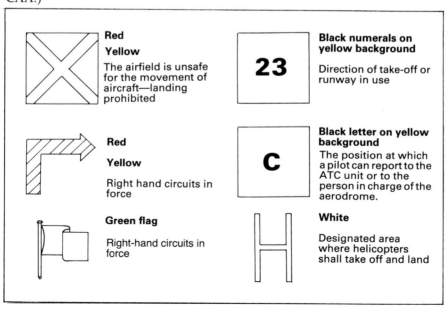

unprecedented rate. Aircraft had to fly at night, in all kinds of weather, do so in quantity and fight as well. Armies were fighting battles many miles from their native shore and had to be serviced and reinforced. In 1942 the first of the really big raids on German cities began, Cologne, Essen, Bremen, Hamburg and other cities were attacked by over 1,000 bombers. As the war continued the attacking force was joined by the USAAF with their massive daylight raids and suddenly the sky was no longer such a big and empty place.

The need to provide some form of control was now very much evident, the airspace around the major airfields was becoming heavily congested and to the losses sustained in combat had to be added those caused by aircraft collisions both in the air and on the

**Below** *The flight deck of a Boeing Stratocruiser. Note the multiplicity of instruments and switches. The direct line of descent from the B–29 Superfortress is clearly evident.* (Boeing Commercial Airplane Company.)
**Above right** *The flight deck of a Boeing 737. A neater layout with flying instruments duplicated to left and right with engine instruments in centre and power levers (throttles) below.* (Boeing Commercial Airplane Company.)
**Below right** *The flight deck of a Boeing 747. A neat and comparatively simple layout for a large aeroplane.* (Boeing Commercial Airplane Company.)

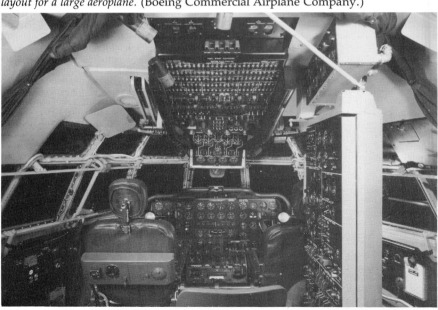

ground. 'Flying control' had been instituted in a limited way prior to World War 2 at some civil and military airfields. This however concerned itself with arriving and departing traffic at a particular airfield, and once away from the airfield the pilot was pretty much on his own. Communication between the aircraft and the flying controller was made in a somewhat rudimentary manner being a mixture of radio and visual signals. Coloured lights, coloured flares and the use of agreed ground signals, set in an area known as the signals square, were the main methods. The signals square was situated close to the flying control building and contained large symbols, easily read from the cockpit of an aircraft flying close to the airfield. They indicated such things as the direction of take-off and landing, the direction of the circuit, and other details which a pilot needed to know. All but out of use today, there is one ground signal which can still be seen on many airfields, oil rigs, and on several naval vessels. It is a large white painted letter H, sometimes contained in a circle, and marks the area where helicopters may take off and land.

Radio communication was also available, initially in the form of wireless telegraphy (WT), using the Morse code and then came radio telephony (RT), using direct voices. Other ideas developed during the war were also to be adopted and developed in the coming ATC system. Radar, which had played such an important part, was to become a vital tool and without it the modern ATC system could not handle the volume of traffic that it does. A development of a radar related device was also to prove to be an equally valuable tool. The radar picture will show any aircraft which the radar aerial 'sees' and cannot discriminate between friendly aircraft and those with hostile intent. To combat this problem and to aid identification of limited information by the observer a system was devised whereby aircraft could switch on a transmitter which caused an additional signal or group of signals to appear on the display. These appeared alongside the blip marking the aircraft, and the system, known as IFF (Identification—Friend or Foe), was the direct predecessor of the current system known as Secondary Surveillance Radar (SSR).

At the end of the war then there was much that could be made available or could be developed to form the basis of a modern ATC system. There was however one very important difference in the situation between the ending of the war in 1918 and that in 1945. Aviation had come of age and reliable aircraft were everywhere

*The flight deck of a Boeing 757. Note the radio and systems control panel in the roof.* (Boeing Commercial Airplane Company.)

available. Long range flights had proved and refined navigational techniques. In the United States in particular aircraft manufacturers had produced a whole range of transport aircraft not only to fly on their own domestic routes by also to transport vast quantities of men and materials to support the war effort being made many miles from home. True, the aircraft had again been used to deliver death and destruction from the skies but it had also shown its potential for use in peace. The aircraft were there, the airfields were there, the crews were there, the Air Traffic Control system was not—but it seemed the world was ready to fly.

**Chapter 2**

# *The regulatory bodies*

In 1944, in anticipation of and in preparation for the peace to come the United States extended an invitation to 55 allied and neutral nations to attend a conference to discuss the future of international civil aviation. In November 1944, 52 of those invited met in Chicago to investigate the political, economic and technical problems, and to find solutions to these where possible. A number of major agreements were to come out of this conference, the main ones being; the International Air Services Transit Agreement, the International Air Transport Agreement and the Convention on International Civil Aviation. The first two of these were to produce agreement on what became known as 'the five freedoms'. Signatories to these agreements extended to each other the following 'freedoms' within their territories:

1 The privilege to overfly without landing.
2 The privilege to land for non-commercial purposes.
3 The privilege to put down passengers, mail and cargo taken on in the territory of registration of the aircraft.
4 The privilege to take on passengers, mail and cargo bound for the territory of registration of the aircraft.
5 The privilege to take on passengers, mail and cargo destined for the territory of any other contracting state and the privilege to put down passengers, mail and cargo coming from any such territory.

The first two agreements thus assured co-operation between signatory states on the conduct and operation of international air transport. The third agreement, the Convention on International Civil Aviation, was popularly termed the Chicago Convention. It laid down 96 articles to establish the privileges and restrictions on contracting states. These were: to provide for the adoption of internationally agreed standards and recommended practices to regulate air navigation; recommend the installation of navigation facilities by member states; suggest the facilitation of air transport by the reduction of customs and immigration formalities and to set up a permanent body known as the International Civil Aviation Organisation (ICAO) charged with the administration of the principles of the Chicago Convention. The Headquarters of ICAO is in Montreal and the organisation is headed by the Assembly, a governing body known as the Council and six additional representative bodies which are:

1 The Air Navigation Commission.
2 The Air Transport Committee.
3 The Legal Committee.
4 The Committee on Joint Support of Air Navigation Services.
5 The Finance Committee.
6 The Committee for Unlawful Interference.

ICAO then was to become the governing body for civil aviation. Its function is to set the standards for aerodromes, telecommunications, navigational aids, air traffic services, search and rescue, aeronautical charts and, most importantly, the Rules of the Air. It also undertakes to lay down minimum standards of safety for the design and construction of aircraft, the training and testing of pilots, navigators, engineers, Air Traffic Control Officers and the operational aspects of aircraft engaged in international flights.

In order that these laudable aims can be put into practice the ICAO Council lays down international standards, recommended practices and procedures for the safety, regularity and efficiency of air navigation. The standards and recommended practices are contained in 18 annexes to the Chicago Convention.

The ICAO 'Standard' covers any specification for physical characteristics, configuration, material, performance, personnel or procedure, the uniform application of which is recognised as necessary for the safety or regularity of international air navigation. Contracting states will comply with these in accordance with the Convention. Should, however, compliance not be possible then notification of this fact to the Council is compulsory under Article 38 of the Convention.

The ICAO 'Recommended Practice' covers exactly the same ground, however in this instance compliance is deemed to be desirable rather than essential. Detailed material is also issued in the

ICAO 'Procedures for Air Navigation Services', adopted by the
Council in accordance with Article 37 of the Convention. This serves
to amplify the basic principles of Standards and Recommended
Practices and embraces aircraft operation, Rules of the Air, Air
Traffic Control, abbreviations and codes.

ICAO also provides assistance to developing countries who,
whilst wishing to conform to international standards, simply do not
have the internal resources to do so. This assistance covers all areas
of civil aviation and can come in the form of the provision of
international experts, instructors, training equipment and overseas
fellowships.

The United Kingdom was, of course, one of the original signatories to the Chicago conference, and set about building its own
organisation to control and regulate aviation both within its boundaries and to and from overseas departure and destination points. It
could be said that one of the characteristics of the British is their
leaning towards evolution rather than revolution. The initial approach was cautious with civil aviation being looked upon with
some suspicion and no government of whatever political persua-
sion being keen to relinquish a very tight hold. From 1945 until 1967
the regulation and control of air transport was variously in the
hands of the Ministry of Transport, Ministy of Transport and Civil
Aviation, Ministry of Aviation, the Board of Trade (Civil Aviation
Division), and the Department of Trade and Industry. In short it
appeared that aviation was really nobody's child and was being
grafted onto whichever government organisation put up the least
resistance!

In 1967 the government of the day decided that this situation
could not and should not continue. A committee was set up under
the Chairmanship of Sir Ronald Edwards to look at the whole
question of civil air transport to include the regulatory aspects. The
committee published its findings in 1969 and one of the most
important of its recommendations was to advise the setting up of
the Civil Aviation Authority. This new authority was to bring
together under one umbrella various aviation functions previously
carried out by such as the Department of Trade and Industry, the
Air Transport Licensing Board and the Air Registration Board. It
was to undertake a positive role in the economic and safety regulation of the aviation industry.

The Civil Aviation Act of 1971 formally set up the new organisation with effect from December 22 1971 and it was to assume its full

responsibilities from April 1 1972. In simplified terms the CAA was to divide its efforts in two main directions. The first of these concerned the regulatory aspects whilst the second concerned the running of a National Air Traffic Control Service (NATS) jointly with the Ministry of Defence. The CAA also acts as the government's expert adviser on aviation matters. Certain areas of responsibility remained with central government, namely international civil aviation relations, accident investigation, policy decisions on aircraft noise problems, national airport development and aviation security.

The original 1971 Act empowered the Secretary of State for Trade to give general guidance to the CAA but the Authority was to maintain a wide measure of discretion with regard to details. However, the Civil Aviation Act of 1980 was to remove this power and the CAA is now required to formulate and publish its own air transport policies and objectives after consultation with the aviation industry and users. CAA policy is decided by a 12 member board, appointed by the Secretary of State for Trade. The CAA currently employs approximately 7,300 people of whom just over three-quarters are employed in NATS. The remaining numbers are divided between the safety and economic aspects of the authority's work. Constitutionally independant of central government, the staff of the CAA are not civil servants.

The CAA was given the financial objective of recovering the whole of its operating costs and to achieve a reasonable return on capital. Essential services to aviation are to be paid for by the user and not by the tax payer, many of whom do not use the services and therefore derive no direct benefit. As with all new business ventures, and in financial terms that is what the CAA was, it was not expected to show any profit in its first years of trading and the trading loss was made good by a government grant. By April 1982 experience gained in charging policy combined with changes made to the basis on which CAA made its cost recovery meant that the grant aid could be dispensed with and the CAA is now self sufficient.

The main bulk of income to the CAA comes from charges made to the user of airport air traffic services, North Atlantic air traffic services, UK airspace air traffic services, economic services, air safety services, and miscellaneous services. Other sources of income include the selling of 'in house' expertise such as the training of overseas students in the UK.

The last full year for which figures are available is 1983. The percentage proportion of income at that time was divided as follows:

| | |
|---|---|
| UK airspace traffic services | 59.2% |
| North Atlantic traffic services | 3.7% |
| CAA Scottish Aerodromes | 3.7% |
| Economic services and miscellaneous | 4.0% |
| Air safety services | 9.8% |
| Airport air traffic services | 19.6% |

Prior to 1971 the payment of costs in the provision of an ATC service was the responsibility of the governments of individual countries. However, with the rapid development of post-war civil aviation this was no longer acceptable. From 1971 arrangements were made for the individual airline carriers to bear part of the cost of provision of an ATC service within Eurocontrol airspace. This airspace comprised that held by the original signatories to the Eurocontrol agreement made in 1960. The signatories were; the United Kingdom, Belgium, Germany, France, Luxembourg and the Netherlands, with Ireland becoming a member state in 1965. Additionally, agreement was made for Eurocontrol to collect route charges on behalf of Austria, Portugal, Switzerland and Spain. Not all flights however are liable to Eurocontrol charges. Flights made under VFR, military flights, flights engaged in search and rescue, aircraft test flights and flights engaged in the testing of ATC facilities are exempt.

Where charging is applicable it is made as a single charge for each flight although the flight may, of course, be made in the airspace of more than one state. To enable these changes to be calculated, data is provided by the airlines to Eurocontrol headquarters in Brussels. Details of flights are also obtained from flight plans and flight progress strips. This includes dates, times and points of departure and arrival, or, where more than one state is involved, point of entry to and exit from the airspace concerned, the aircraft type and the operator's identity. Data on scheduled flights is also provided to obviate the need to deal individually with repetative data. The operators undertake an annual review of the data supplied.

Daily returns are produced by Eurocontrol, listing flights by operator, and these are subsequently totalled on a monthly basis and distributed to the operators concerned. The actual charge is based upon a formula involving the distance flown within Eurocontrol airspace and the weight of the aircraft, resulting in the operator receiving an account as their share of the operating cost.

The government has certain obligations for aviation in the international field and these are vested in the Department of Trade for civil matters and in the Ministry of Defence for military matters. These exercise overall policy control and on their behalf NATS discharges the operational, technical and financial air traffic service commitments arising from the UK membership of ICAO and the European Organisation for the Safety of Air Navigation (Eurocontrol) and the NATO Committee for European Airspace Co-ordination (CEAC).

The foregoing is, of necessity, a somewhat brief and simplified explanation of some of the international aviation activities in which the CAA plays a part. It will be seen that the CAA does a whole lot more than just employ people who 'talk down' the aircraft, but a detailed description of these functions has no place in this particular book.

# Chapter 3

# *Communication*

The function of the United Kingdom air traffic service can be summed up in one succinct phrase; to provide a safe, orderly and expeditious flow of air traffic within United Kingdom airspace. This is a little like saying that if you want to go Grand Prix motor racing it is a good idea to have a driving licence! The simple statement serves to hide a massively complicated methodology. Many individual parts go to make up the whole of an ATC system, however there is one underlying theme common to them all and that is the need to communicate information. The whole of the air traffic service relies upon efficient communications, be they spoken, written, or via some technical medium. The method of communication might be by voice, by pieces of paper, by teleprinter, by electronic data display, by closed circuit television or by any combination of these. There is no hard and fast rule about which method must be used. Generally the chosen method is the one which works and is found to be the most efficient for the particular task.

The content of the communication however is dictated not only by the quantity of information to be passed but equally importantly by the time available in which to collate it, transmit it, and absorb the content upon receipt. To help meet these requirements an internationally agreed set of codes and abbreviations is used. This is particularly time efficient when compiling and transmitting messages. Those who work within the ATC system quickly learn to memorise the most common codes and formats but to an outsider it can appear that little of what is written and much of what is spoken has been abbreviated to point a where it is beyond comprehension. The idea of using internationally accepted and understood codes is not, of course, new. In the days when most radio communication was by wireless telegraphy using the Morse code many repetitive messages were brought into a system known as the Q code. The first letter was always Q followed by two additional letters to signify a particular part of the code. Even today certain parts of the Q code remain in use because they convey exactly what is meant. Some examples and their meanings are:

**QDM** The magnetic heading for you to steer to reach me (or——) with no wind was——degrees (at——time).

**QDR** Your magnetic bearing from me (or from——) was—— degrees (at——time).

**QFE** If you set the subscale of your altimeter to read——milli-bars, the instrument would indicate its height above aerodrome elevation.

**QNH** If you set the subscale of your altimeter to read——millibars, the instrument would indicate its elevation (above sea level) if your aircraft were on the ground at my station.

**QSY** Change to transmit on another frequency on——kHz or mHz.

*A typical VHF radio mast of a type to be seen all over the country.*

To maximise the amount of data that can be transmitted, and at the same time to minimise the physical length and content of any message, the adoption of coding allows the best use to be made of what can be heavily congested message routeing systems. The United Kingdom employs a system known as the Aeronautical Fixed Telecommunications Network or AFTN to pass messages by teleprinter between stations. The AFTN is also connected to a similar international system so that messages can be sent to or received from almost any point in the world. The full list of codes and abbreviations used in compiling information forms a book in itself. However in order to demonstrate the system a few examples are given here.

### Location indicators

| | | | |
|---|---|---|---|
| **EGAA** | Belfast (Aldergrove) | **EHAM** | Amsterdam |
| **EGHH** | Bournemouth (Hurn) | **EBBR** | Brussels |
| **EGPH** | Edinburgh (Turnhouse) | **EKCH** | Copenhagen |
| **EGFF** | Glamorgan (Rhoose) | **KJFK** | New York (Kennedy) |
| **EGJJ** | Jersey | **EDDF** | Frankfurt |
| **EGLL** | London (Heathrow) | **UUEE** | Moscow |
| **EGKK** | London (Gatwick) | **LEPA** | Palma |
| **EGCC** | Manchester | **ESSA** | Stockholm |

The basic group of four letters identifies the point of origin/destination but simply addressing a message in this manner is not specific enough. To the basic four letter group can be added additional pairs of letters. For example a message bound for the Air Traffic Control tower at Dublin would be addressed EIDWZT. Other additional pairs of letters are:

| | | | |
|---|---|---|---|
| **ZA** | Approach Control | **ZH** | Helicopter Control |
| **ZO** | Oceanic Control | **ZR** | Area Control Service |

### Company Callsigns

Airline operators also need to know about the movement of their own aircraft or those for which they have a handling agreement. Abbreviated company callsigns are used, a few examples being:

| | | | |
|---|---|---|---|
| **AC** | Air Canada | **EI** | Aer Lingus |
| **AF** | Air France | **JL** | Japanese Airlines |
| **BA** | British Airways | **KL** | KLM |
| **BD** | British Midland | **LY** | El Al |
| **DA** | Dan Air | **PA** | Pan American |

| SR | Swissair | SK | SAS |

One further pair of letters can still be added when necessary. A message referring to an Aer Lingus aircraft departing from Manchester to Copenhagen would include amongst the addresses EIDWEIOO where the airline's parent operations office is being addressed.

## Aircraft type designators

Similarly aircraft types themselves are identified by internationally recognised codes. If this were not so it is easy to appreciate the confusion that could be caused if there was no way of knowing in advance if an incoming aircraft identified as COM was really a Commanche or a Comet. Examples are:

| | | | |
|---|---|---|---|
| **BN2** | BN Islander | **A300** | Airbus |
| **BE55** | Beech Baron | **B707** | Boeing 707 |
| **DC3** | Douglas Dakota | **B747** | Boeing 747 |
| **PA31** | Piper Navajo | **CONC** | Concorde |
| **FK27** | Fokker Friendship | **HS25** | Hawker Siddley 125 |
| **HP7** | Handley Page Herald | **TU04** | Tupolev 104 |

The foregoing examples are not meant to be comprehensive but serve to illustrate the system. Further examples of abbreviations and codes will be encountered in later chapters together with their explanation and more detailed lists of some of these will be found in the appendices.

Voice communication can be anything from a comment between two people to an exchange involving many miles of telephone wire, micro-wave radio links, or even satellites. When using radio telephones or ordinary telephones it is necessary to ensure that the listener cannot be confused. The frequency or line may be subject to interference or the listener may have a loud background of engine noise to contend with. In order to ensure clarity of meaning it is sometimes necessary to spell all or part of a message. If this is the case the ICAO word spelling alphabet is used. The pronunciation is shown in parentheses with the syllable to be stressed underlined.

| | | | | |
|---|---|---|---|---|
| **A** | Alpha (<u>AL</u> FAH) | | **F** | Foxtrot (<u>FOKS</u> TROT) |
| **B** | Bravo (<u>BRAH</u> <u>VOH</u>) | | **G** | Golf (GOLF) |
| **C** | Charlie (<u>CHAR</u> LEE) | | **H** | Hotel (HOH <u>TELL</u>) |
| **D** | Delta (<u>DELL</u> TAH) | | **I** | India (<u>IN</u> DEE AH) |
| **E** | Echo (<u>ECK</u> HO) | | **J** | Juliet (<u>JEW</u> LEE <u>ETT</u>) |

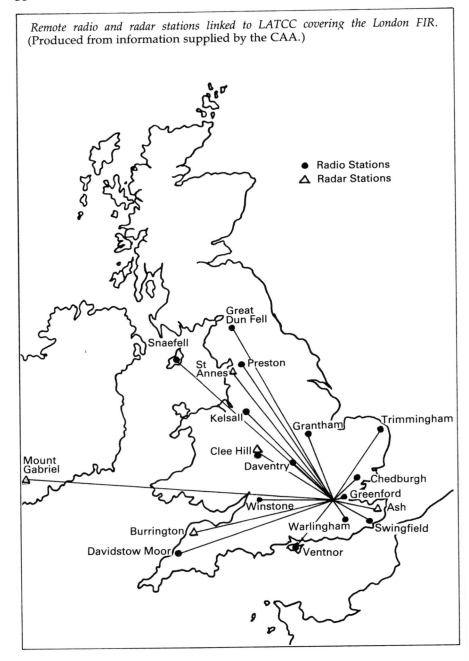

*Remote radio and radar stations linked to LATCC covering the London FIR.* (Produced from information supplied by the CAA.)

| K | Kilo (<u>KEY</u> LOH) | S | Sierra (SEE <u>AIR</u> RAH) |
|---|---|---|---|
| L | Lima (<u>LEE</u> MAH) | T | Tango (<u>TANG</u> GO) |
| M | Mike (MIKE) | U | Uniform (<u>YOU</u> NEE FORM) |
| N | November (NO <u>VEM</u> BER) | V | Victor (<u>VIK</u> TAH) |
| O | Oscar (<u>OSS</u> CAH) | W | Whiskey (<u>WISS</u> KEY) |
| P | Papa (PAH <u>PAH</u>) | X | Xray (<u>ACKS</u> <u>RAY</u>) |
| Q | Quebec (KEH <u>BECK</u>) | Y | Yankee (<u>YANG</u> KEY) |
| R | Romeo (<u>ROW</u> ME OH) | Z | Zulu (<u>ZOO</u> LOO) |

**Numerals**

| 0 | <u>ZE RO</u> | 5 | <u>FIFE</u> |
|---|---|---|---|
| 1 | <u>WUN</u> | 6 | <u>SIX</u> |
| 2 | <u>TOO</u> | 7 | <u>SEVEN</u> |
| 3 | <u>TREE</u> | 8 | <u>AIT</u> |
| 4 | <u>FOWER</u> | 9 | <u>NINER</u> |

**Thousand** <u>TOU</u> <u>SAND</u>        **Decimal** <u>DAY</u> SEE <u>MAL</u>

A controller's position would normally have a number of frequencies available, each one selectable by a switch. A three position key is also provided; in the centre position the channel is on receive, it has to be pressed down in order to transmit and by pushing the key up intercom facilities are available between positions. Both radio and intercom exchanges are recorded automatically and can be played back if the need arises in say the investigation of an 'air miss'.

Since the coming of the computer into ATC more and more information has been made available by data display. This has certain advantages in that a number of positions can use a single display. On black and white displays it can be difficult to pick out the information relevent to your particular task but this problem can now be overcome by using colour displays where the data can be sectionalised by the use of discreet colour. It is of course extremely important that displays of this nature are highly reliable. A failed domestic television set is a nuisance, failure of an operational display will certainly cause a certain amount of consternation at best.

One other form of communication should be discussed at this juncture. Lost in history is the identity of the person who, probably by accident, invented the wheel. This was one of those all too rare occasions when the principle at least was exactly right from the start. ATC also has a remarkable device which, in principle, has proved very difficult to better and that is the flight progress strip.

**Aerodrome departing flights. IFR plan**      Background colour—blue

| A | B | | F | G | H | I | | K | L | M |
| C | D | E | | | J | | | | | |

| | | 160 | BE100 GAYGY T260 | 41 | 42 | | R 80 M▸ STF RLCE 160 43 | | | 23 P T |
| 17⁴⁰ | 47 | | | A1-W9-DW9 EGPT | | | | | | 127·45/50 |

A—Vacant or aerodrome abbreviation if the departure is from a subsidiary airfield
B—Planned cruising level
C—Estimated time of departure
D—Actual time of departure
E—Vacant
F—Aircraft type—identity—cruising true air speed

G—Time clearance requested from ATCC
H—Time clearance received
I—Time of revised clearance if issued
J—Planned route and destination
K—Clearance received from ATCC
L—Space for revised clearance
M—Controller's notes

In the example shown the aircraft is cleared via Stafford (reporting point), Amber 1, White 9, Delta White 9 to Perth. It is cleared to climb under Radar Control to FL 80 and maintain, to request a flight level change en-route. It is not cleared to take off until 17.43. Box M shows the runway in use, that the aircraft has been given the QNH/QFE and a time check. It also shows the airways frequency and the time the aircraft changed to it

**Airways crossing strip**                      Background colour—pink

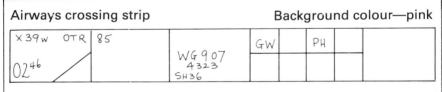

| X 39 W   OTR | 85 | | | GW | | PH | | |
| 02⁴⁶ | / | | WG 907 4323 SH36 | | | | | |

This strip is for an SH36, callsign Loganair 907 flying from Luton to Edinburgh and crossing airway Blue 1 39 nautical miles west of Ottringham at 02:46 at FL85

**Flight Information Region strip**             Background colour—blue

| | C404 HBD 001 | GW EIDW | 60 | KN1 01⁵² | TOLKA 02⁴³ | | | X A25 60 EIDW/33 |
| | | | | | 58 | | | |

This type of strip is used for traffic flying off airways in the FIR, in this case from Luton to Dublin at FL 60. The aircraft estimated crossing airway Amber 25 at 01:52 and actually crossed at 01:58. It was transferred to Dublin at 33 minutes past the hour.

A—Estimated time for fix—computer identification number—sector number
B—Fix position
C—Flight level information
D—Aircraft identification—assigned SSR code—wake turbulence category—aircraft
   type—SSR fit—true airspeed
E—Sector Controller's scribble box
F—Departure aerodrome—route and destination—previous fix and time—requested
   level and date

| 1302  56  120 | 1OM | /58 ↑  / 30 / | 23o | BA5481  5437  M/BA11/C  T435 | WAL - 3TF - GX  EGAA  R3  EGBB | ..... BEL  1253  230  MD7 |
|---|---|---|---|---|---|---|

This strip is for a British Airways BAC1–11 flying from Belfast to Birmingham along airway Red 3 routeing Belfast—Isle of Man—Wallasey—Stafford—GX (Birmingham beacon) and is placed under the IOM designator. A similar strip is produced for each reporting point along the route. The callsign would be printed in red to indicate an eastbound flight. The controller's strip marking in box C would be made in red ink showing that the aircraft was climbing to FL 230 with checks through FL 130 and FL 150

**Above** *Example of a computer generated (9020D) flight progress strip.* (Produced from information supplied by the CAA.)

**Above left** *Diagram showing how a flight progress strip contains a condensed record of intended and actual events.* (Produced from information supplied by the CAA.)

**Below left** *Further examples of flight progress strips.* (Produced from information supplied by the CAA.)

This remarkable strip of paper has been around for years and even in the age of computers, microchip revolutions and all the other phrases beloved of those who are devotees of such things, the flight progress strip survives. These strips of paper form a code in themselves, indicated by their colour. For example, information on outbound aircraft is written on a blue aerodrome strip whilst that on inbound aircraft is written on a buff strip. The strips are divided into various boxes each one being allocated a function. The result is that on one piece of paper a complete history can be written. This shows not only intention but also what actually happened and it is easily handled and stored for future reference. The strips are held in specially designed holders and placed on a strip board. In an Air Traffic Control Tower a typical flight progress board layout in front of the Tower Controller might consist of three boards where the left hand one contains buff strips on expected inbound traffic, the right hand one contains blue strips on expected departures, and the centre board contains strips on 'live' traffic under his control. This middle board would contain strips of both colours in order of movement as befits the task which is to integrate arriving and departing traffic.

In practice the strip has many unofficial but very practical uses and herein lies its versatility. If, as an Air Traffic Control Assistant, you wish to draw the Air Traffic Controller's attention to a particularly important point or unusual situation, you can resort to all manner of 'attention getters', especially when he is busy. These can vary from leaving the strip holder sticking up at one end, putting the holder in the board upside down, or, in extreme cases, poking him in the ribs with it. It is however as well to have some very good reason for the latter action! It is also a matter of record that the strip holders themselves make an excellent device for removing ice from car windows at the conclusion of a winter night shift, but I digress.

A great many strips are hand written and at places where there is no direct computer involvement they are placed in holders of a neutral colour. To avoid complications with computer printed strips, these are all the same colour and in this case the holders themselves are coloured. Single strips are used mainly in aerodrome and approach work but in the ATCC field a flight will be covered by a number of strips, one for each reporting point on the route. Some examples of strips and their uses are given at the end of this chapter.

Communications then are very much the name of the game and form an unbroken thread through all of the ATC system. Whatever form they take they must be both efficient and reliable. A jet airliner in level flight covers eight miles in every minute and time is rarely on the side of the Air Traffic Controller. He must make quick decisions and cannot waste time trying to decypher messages, nor must his instructions be misunderstood. For this reason much of the phraseology used in ATC is laid down to a rigid format which can often sound strange to the ear of the listener not used to the same form of discipline in his own occupation. Hopefully, by the end of this book some understanding will have been given.

**Chapter 4**

# *Rules of the air and divisions of airspace*

Before looking at the individual elements of the ATC system it is necessary to look at the divisions of airspace and the various rules and regulations governing its use. United Kingdom airspace encompasses some 350,000 square miles over the earth's surface and is divided into two Flight Information Regions or FIRs. These are the London FIR and the Scottish FIR. Within these FIRs, NATS provides a legally protected structure of controlled airspace designed to accommodate the flight paths of the main body of traffic. Outside of this formalised structure NATS encourages the maximum flexibility for those flying outside controlled or advisory airspace. Controlled airspace also takes in the Terminal Control Areas (TMA) which enclose the main airports or groups of airports. Airways are designated corridors usually about ten miles wide and have a vertical extension from around 3,000 ft up to 24,500 ft above mean sea level (amsl). The centreline of each airway is marked by radio beacons of differing types but all known as 'point source' aids. To fly within controlled airspace a pilot has to be properly licensed, must file a flight plan, is subject to instructions from Air Traffic Control and his aircraft must be equipped with the necessary navigational and communications equipment, as laid down in the Air Navigation Order (1980) and the Air Navigation (General) Regulations 1981.

Above 24,500 ft and up to 66,000 ft in the whole of UK airspace civil traffic is subject to a full and mandatory ATC service. Civil aircraft are not alone in the sky however so that almost all of the same airspace is also designated as a military Mandatory Radar Service Area (MRSA) within which military aircraft are required to receive a radar control service. Both of the above are designated as special rules airspace. In addition it has proved necessary to provide

**Following page** *Division of airspace into Flight Information Regions.* (Produced from information supplied by the CAA.)

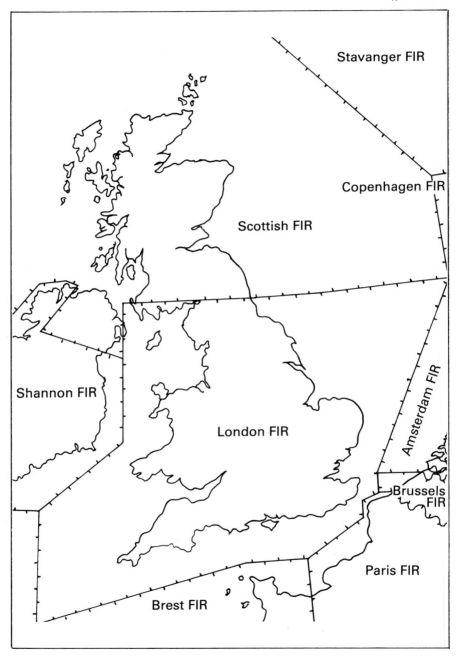

Stavanger FIR

Copenhagen FIR

Scottish FIR

Shannon FIR

Amsterdam FIR

London FIR

Brussels FIR

Paris FIR

Brest FIR

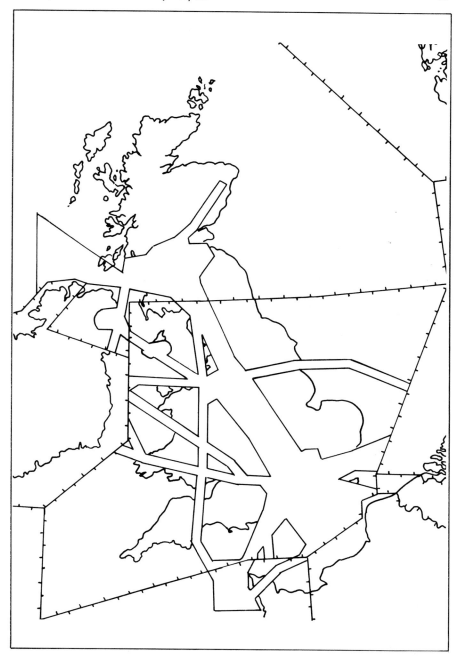

**Previous page** *Disposition of controlled airspace within the UK FIR boundaries.*
(Produced from information supplied by the CAA.)

special rules airspace at a number of places where there is a need to protect public transport aircraft without undue restriction on the movements of other aircraft. Aircraft flying in this airspace are required to carry suitable radio equipment so that the pilot can advise ATC of his presence and comply with ATC instructions.

In other airspace NATS provides an ATC service to aircraft on request. The traffic on some routes is not heavy enough to justify the status of an airway, nonetheless it is sufficient to warrant some sort of regulation to enhance safety. These are known as advisory routes and pilots flying on these routes will receive an ATC service which ensures separation between themselves and all other participating traffic. Within this airspace, from 24,500 ft down to 8,000 ft and occasionally below, NATS provide an advisory radar separation service to any aircraft on request provided that the aircraft is within range of one of the NATS radars. Below 8,000 ft Ministry of Defence units participate in a Lower Airspace Radar Service (LARS) supplementing the NATS service to any civil or military aircraft flying in the vicinity of a military aerodrome.

Two further services are available to pilots throughout the whole airspace whether controlled or uncontrolled. NATS provides a Flight Information Service (FIS) to airborne aircraft and an Aeronautical Information Service (AIS) to pilots on the ground. Together these services offer a whole range of information necessary for the conduct of safe flight.

Outside of domestic airspace, and as agreed by ICAO, the United Kingdom is responsible for providing an ATC service to aircraft in transit over the north-east corner of the Atlantic Ocean eastwards of Longitude 30° W. NATS in conjunction with ATC authorities of the USA, Canada, Portugal, and Iceland operates an upper airspace track system designed to operate on the same principle as used on airways, providing an air traffic separation and information service to all aircraft crossing the ocean.

Flights by civil aircraft within UK airspace can only be conducted according to either Visual Flight Rules (VFR) or Instrument Flight Rules (IFR). A pilot must fly according to the Instrument Flight Rules if: the airspace has been notified as one which permits only that type of flight; if the meteorological conditions preclude flight according to the visual flight rules; or at night.

Before going further it is probably as well to explain the meaning of four sets of initials that together cause more confusion than almost anything else, they are IMC, VMC, IFR and VFR. Confusion can be avoided if it is remembered that the first two, IMC (Instrument Meteorological Conditions) and VMC (Visual Meteorological Conditions) are conditions imposed by nature and all the legislation in the world won't alter the fact that the cloud is on the deck and the rain is pouring down! IFR (Instrument Flight Rules) and VFR (Visual Flight Rules) on the other hand are man-made rules and whilst it is not permitted to fly VFR at night it is entirely possible to fly in VMC at night. The pilot of an aircraft is responsible for determining whether or not the weather conditions in his area permit flight in accordance with VFR. To enable him to do this certain minimum conditions have to be satisfied. Inside or outside of controlled

*Weather criteria for flight in Visual Meteorological Conditions. With a forward visibility from the flight deck of not less than five nautical miles, a horizontal distance from cloud of not less than one nautical mile and a vertical distance from cloud of not less than 1,000 ft, both above and below the aircraft, the pilot may conduct his flight in VMC.*

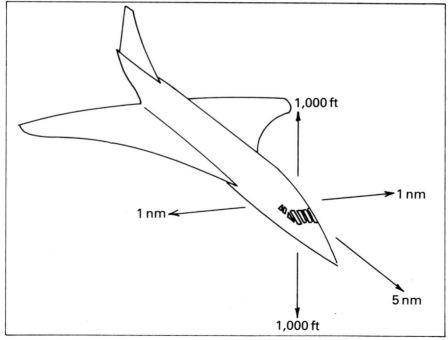

1,000 ft

1 nm

1 nm

5 nm

1,000 ft

| Quadrantal rule flights at levels below FL 245 | | Semi-circular rule flights at levels above FL 245 | |
|---|---|---|---|
| 359 ┬ 360 | | 359 ┬ 360 | |
| FL 45, 65, 85, 105 etc up to FL 225 | FL 30, 50, 70, 90 etc up to FL 230 | FL 260 and 280 FL 310, 350, 390, 430 etc | FL 250, 270 and 290 FL 330, 370, 410, 450 etc |
| 270 | 089 | | |
| 269 | 090 | | |
| FL 40, 64, 80, 100 etc up to FL 240 | FL 35, 55, 75, 95 etc up to FL 235 | | |
| 180 ┴ 179 | | 180 ┴ 179 | |

It should be noted that above FL 290 the vertical separation between aircraft is increased to 2,000 ft. This is because the barometric altimeter is less accurate as the altitude increases

*Diagram explaining the quadrantal rule and semi-circular rule for flights outside controlled airspace.* (Produced from information supplied by the CAA.)

airspace and above 3,000 ft amsl the aircraft has to be one mile horizontally from cloud, 1,000 ft vertically clear of cloud both above and below and to have a flight visibility of not less than five miles. At or below 3,000 ft amsl the horizontal and vertical distances remain the same but the flight visibility minimum is reduced to three miles. Aircraft flying at 140 kt or less should be clear of cloud, in sight of the surface with a minimum flight visibility of one mile. Helicopters are required to be clear of cloud and in sight of the surface.

Regardless of whether or not a flight is made in VMC, where a pilot has to conduct a flight according to IFR he must obey the following conditions. Within controlled airspace he must file a flight plan and obtain an ATC clearance before proceeding with that flight. He must conduct that flight in accordance with clearances and instructions from ATC. He must maintain a listening watch on the appropriate radio frequencies and report the position of his aircraft to ATC according to published procedures. Outside con-trolled airspace he must comply with the quadrantal or semi-circular rule when in level flight above 3,000 ft amsl. The altimeter is set to 1013.2 millibars and the cruising level selected according to the magnetic track. Variations from this may however be made if the aircraft is in a holding pattern according to published procedures or is otherwise instructed by ATC.

In many parts of the world, including the United Kingdom, flight is only permitted in controlled airspace in accordance with IFR procedures. As previously stated this ruling applies irrespective of actual weather conditions at the time the flight is made. In order that the smaller and less well equipped aircraft can be allowed to penetrate controlled airspace a special category of flight, known as Special Visual Flight Rules (SVFR) can be requested by the pilot. The pilot need not file a flight plan but must give brief details of the aircraft type, callsign and intention. A full flight plan will however be required if the pilot wishes his destination airfield to be notified of his flight.

A pilot may also use a very simple form of notification known as 'booking out'. In this instance he is only required to state his

*Vertical division of airspace.* (Produced from information supplied by the CAA.)

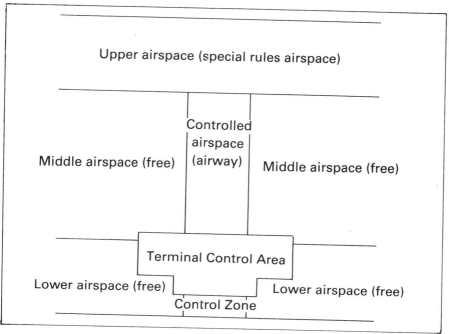

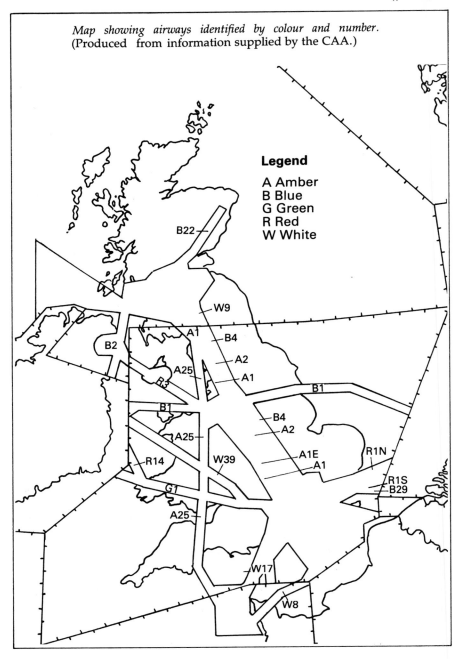

*Map showing airways identified by colour and number.*
(Produced from information supplied by the CAA.)

**Legend**

A Amber
B Blue
G Green
R Red
W White

intention to fly and, within controlled airspace, couple this to a request for a SVFR clearance. At airfields outside of controlled airspace he obtains a clearance to take off and leave the Aerodrome Traffic Zone (ATZ). In either case, once clear of the zone or controlled airspace he is on his own as far as an air traffic service is concerned and provided that he does not intend to penetrate controlled airspace at some future point in the flight and obeys such standing rules as that governing minimum height, he can fly how and where he pleases. The drawback to all of this is, of course, that if anything should go wrong during the flight then the air traffic service will not initiate any search procedures. Even today there are quite large areas in the UK which are well away from main roads and are sparsely populated. In such a landscape a small aircraft is really difficult to see, especially if it has been flown into a hillside.

In order to identify them better and to minimise the sequence of numbers, airways are identified by a colour coding. Although expansion of the airways system has served to confuse the situation in certain areas it is still true to say that, in the main, the colour identity is applied as follows.

Amber airways—run North/South.
Green airways—run East/West.
Blue airways—run East/West.
Red airways—run North-west/South-east and North-east/South-west
White airways—UK FIRs only—seasonal.

There is one other colour in use which applies only within UK airspace and that is purple. A colour historically associated with Royalty, it is used to denote airspace which has been notified for use by a Royal Flight. A Royal Flight is the movement of an aircraft carrying one or more members of the Royal Family who qualify for flights of this status. Headed by HM The Queen, the list includes nominated members of her immediate family. Occasionally other members of the Royal Family, other reigning Sovereigns, Prime Ministers and Heads of State may be afforded Royal Flight status. Such flights are not necessarily always undertaken in aircraft belonging to the Queen's Flight.

Royal Flights in fixed wing aircraft are always provided with controlled airspace to cover the entire flight path whilst the aircraft is in UK airspace. To obtain this coverage Purple airways are established for the entire route and, if needs be, special control

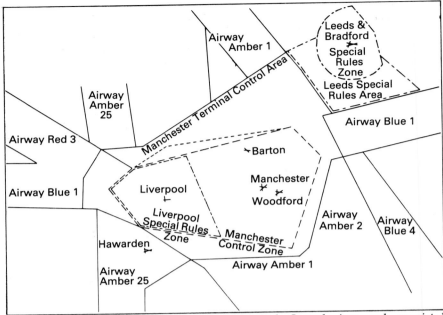

*Simplified map showing Control Zone, Terminal Control Area and associated airways around Manchester and Liverpool airports. (Produced from information supplied by the CAA.)*

zones are also established at departure and destination aerodromes. The Purple airway, like its less exhalted companions, is 10 miles wide but the vertical extent will be laid down at the time. Normal separation standards apply but priority should be given to a Royal Flight so as not to cause undue delay. Royal Flights in helicopters will not have Purple airspace established for their benefit, or special control zones, for that portion of the flight which occurs outside of already established controlled airspace. However a Royal Low Level Corridor will be established and all air traffic service units on or adjacent to the helicopter's route will be advised well in advance. An Aerodrome Control Unit is expected to anticipate a request by the Royal helicopter for clearance through the Aerodrome Traffic Zone.

## Aerodrome Traffic Zone

This extends 3,000 yd from the airfield boundary in any direction and has a vertical extent from ground level up to 2,000 ft. It is designed to protect arriving and departing traffic and aircraft in the circuit from other aircraft in low level transit. Although theoretically there is a traffic zone at every airfield, in practice it only applies where there is no other form of protected airspace.

## Control Zones

These are established around busy airfields and are usually within a Terminal Area complex. They have a vertical extent from ground level up to 2,500 ft or to the base of the Terminal Area. Control Zones are designed to protect the flight paths of aircraft arriving from, or departing to the Terminal Area.

## Terminal Areas

These are established around one or more busy airfields and have a vertical extent from 2,500 ft or the top of the Control Zone, to a height of 24,500 ft, always referred to in ATC jargon as FL 245. In plan view the Terminal Area extends horizontally to connect with the system of airways which serve it and again protects the flight

*Diagram showing the relationship between the Control Zone, the Terminal Control Area and airways. (Produced from information supplied by the CAA.)*

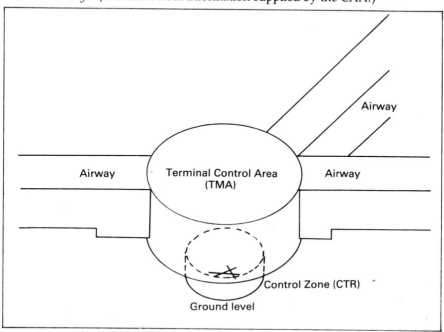

Airway

Airway  Terminal Control Area (TMA)  Airway

Control Zone (CTR)

Ground level

paths of aircraft arriving from or departing to the airways system. system.

## Airways
These connect the main areas of population within the UK FIRs and extend over the boundaries of adjacent FIRs belonging to those States whose boundaries are common to the United Kingdom. They are usually ten miles wide and have a vertical extent from around 3,000 ft to Fl 245, the base of Upper Air Space. The lower limit of an airway will vary according to geographical need, there being no logical reason for having a protected corridor with a great big mountain sticking up into it!

## Upper Air Space
This is an area above FL 245 extending vertically to FL 660 and is designated as a special rules area. Within this area are established Upper Air Routes most, but not all of which, follow the network of airways established below.

## Special Rules Airspace
This is established to protect flights outside controlled airspace proper but where the amount of traffic dictates that such protection be provided.

## Flight Information Region
This is the airspace outside Control Zones, Terminal Areas, Airways and special rules areas. Aircraft are free to fly without being subject to Air Traffic Control procedures and of course they do not then avail themselves of the protection such procedures provide.

Put together, the various elements of controlled airspace provide a basic structure within which it is possible to build an Air Traffic Control system. This structure is international in its extent, crossing national boundaries and seas so that very long range flights are possible entirely within protected airspace. Exactly how a pilot stays within the airways system will be discussed in a later chapter. En-route navigational aids and systems, communications, and an Air Traffic Control organisation are the necessary basic ingredients with which to build an Air Traffic Control service.

The practice of Air Traffic Control has sometimes been referred to as an 'art'. It has also been described as three dimensional chess played at high speed. In truth it is both.

# Chapter 5

## *Separation standards*

It will be remembered that the purpose of the Air Traffic Control service is to provide a safe, orderly, and expeditious flow of air traffic. To assist in this process the contracting states of ICAO have agreed a set of separation standards to be applied internationally. Aircraft may be separated vertically, horizontally, or of course, both. The most straight forward separation to describe is that used to achieve vertical separation. Up to FL 290 aircraft must be separated by not less than 1,000 ft and above FL 290 by not less than 2,000 ft. The increase in the separation standard above FL 290 is made necessary by the fact that the barometric altimeter has a certain amount of in-built error which increases with height.

The term 'Flight Level' or FL which has already been referred to should be given some explanation at this point. The barometric altimeter fitted to an aircraft works on exactly the same principle as the barometer that can often be found hanging in the hallway of a house. The difference is that whereas the domestic barometer registers changes in air pressure at its location and indicates weather trends, the airborne barometer or altimeter is calibrated to show height from zero upwards. The altimeter also has the facility to input a given barometric pressure so that, in effect, it can be adjusted to show height from differing datums. For example, if the known barometric pressure setting, expressed in millibars, for sea level is input to an altimeter of an aircraft parked on an airfield some way above sea level the altimeter will register a height even though the aircraft is firmly on the ground. This is because the datum point is at sea level. An altimeter set in this way is said to be set to the QNH. If however the known pressure setting at aerodrome level is input the altimeter will indicate zero and is said to be set to the QFE.

Most readers will be familiar with the weather map as shown on television, and will have noted the figures present along with the

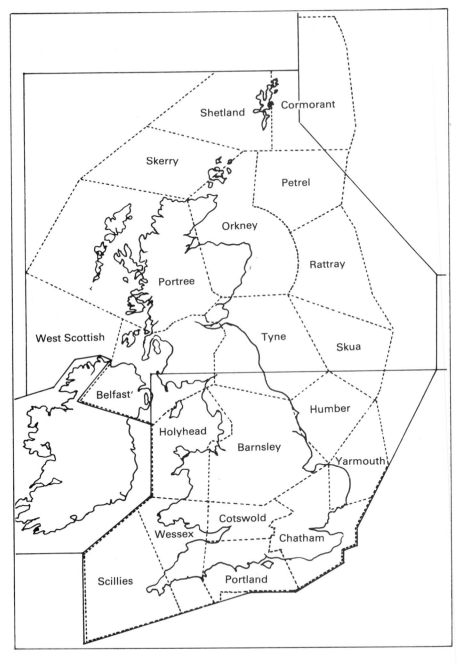

labelling of a weather system as a high or a low. These figures indicate the air pressure expressed in millibars and it will also be noted that these figures can differ markedly over a relatively short distance. It will be appreciated then that difficulty could be experienced in applying altitude or height separation standards as an aircraft transitted along its flight path. In order to maintain a constant reading on the altimeter the aircraft would actually have to climb or descend as it passed through the different areas of barometric pressure. To combat this problem a number of altimeter setting regions have been established, the geographical extent of which are determined by agreement between ATC and the Meteorological Office. The latter advises ATC of the pressure values throughout a particular region and it is the lowest of these which is expressed as the regional QNH. Aircraft leaving an aerodrome are instructed by ATC to change to the QNH whilst aircraft arriving at an aerodrome are instructed by ATC to change to QFE. An aircraft will often transit across the boundaries of one or more of these altimeter setting regions and in order to avoid constant changes of altimeter settings a constant pressure datum is used. This uses a value of 1013.2 millibars and is known internationally as the standard pressure setting. When using this value all heights are expressed as Flight Levels. The change from the regional QNH to the standard pressure setting takes place upon instruction from ATC and the change usually occurs at a height of 4 – 6,000 ft. There exists a somewhat complicated procedure for ensuring that an aircraft using the QNH has adequate separation from an aircraft that may have just changed to the standard pressure setting and also to maintain clearance from the surrounding terrain. However it is sufficient to state here that the objective is always to have a minimum vertical separation of 1,000 ft.

The following may prove useful in getting the various terms into context:

With the altimeter set to 1013.2 millibars the height of the aircraft is expressed as a Flight Level.

With the altimeter set to the regional QNH the height of the aircraft is expressed as an altitude.

With the altimeter set to the QFE the height of the aircraft is expressed as height.

**Left** *Altimeter setting regions within United Kingdom airspace.* (Produced from information supplied by the CAA.)

It is worthy of note that just to make life interesting and to ensure that everyone is still awake, a lot of American built or instrumented aircraft do not use the input of the barometric pressure expressed in millibars. Instead they use inches of mercury as a means of calibration. There is of course a direct correlation between the two methods, the equivalent of 1013.2 millibars being 29.92 inches of mercury. It is the same thing, done differently.

The horizontal separation of aircraft is, unfortunately, and for a variety of reasons not nearly so simple. The three types of horizontal separation are lateral separation, longitudinal separation and radar separation.

Lateral separation can be achieved either by track separation or geographical separation. The former is obtained by requiring aircraft to fly on specified tracks which are separated by a minimum horizontal distance dependant upon the type of navigational aid being used. The latter is achieved by positive position reports over different geographical locations made with either visual reference or by using a navigational aid.

Longitudinal separation is based upon time or distance to ensure that the spacing between the positions of aircraft is never less than that laid down as a minimum. For example, when two aircraft are flying on the same track and at the same cruising flight level the minimum time separation between them must not be less than five minutes provided that the leading aircraft has filed an airspeed of 20 kt or more faster than the following aircraft. If there is no difference in speed then the separation in time is 10 minutes. Similarly, if the first example is applied to two aircraft departing from the same airfield then a time interval of five minutes would be required between their departure times. If however, immediately after take-off, their respective tracks were to diverge by 45° or more then a time separation of one minute would be acceptable. These separation standards are certainly safe and orderly, but expeditious they are not. To further illustrate this consider four inter-continental jet airliners flying along the same air route at the same height when not under radar control. They will cruise at around 480 kt or eight miles in every minute. With a time separation of ten minutes those four aircraft effectively sterilise 240 miles of track distance because they are a minimum of 80 miles apart.

However, by using radar with the ability to positively identify aircraft it is possible to reduce the horizontal separation considerably. Thus the minumum horizontal separation, with both aircraft positively identified, is reduced to five miles. This results in a great increase in the utilisation of airspace and so a far greater volume of traffic can be accommodated in a given volume of airspace. There are also occasions when radar separation can be reduced to three miles but this is dependant upon a number of factors including the distance of the aircraft from the radar aerial. There is absolutely no doubt that without the application of radar to the ATC system the development of air travel as it exists today would not have been possible.

Before leaving separation standards there is one other area where positive separation has to be employed. For some time the need for it was not fully appreciated and more than one pilot acquired a few grey hairs because of this lack of understanding. With the coming of the wide-bodied jet transports, popularly collectivised as 'Jumbos', it has become necessary to ensure that other lighter or smaller aircraft were not positioned or allowed to cross too close to the track of the Jumbo. Aircraft such as the Boeing 747, 767, DC 10, or the Tri-Star (Lockheed 1011) disturb a vast quantity of air by their passing and this disturbance manifests itself as a series of wake vortices. In plain language this means that a Jumbo trails behind it two or more spiralling columns of air which cover large areas and move at considerable rotational speed. The power of these wake vortices is sufficient to overturn a following smaller aircraft or at best to cause extreme difficulty in control. This phenomenon is bad enough at altitude but is considerably more dangerous at lower levels such as on a final approach. In order to bring into being a practical scheme to overcome this problem all types of aircraft have been fitted into the categories of heavy, medium, small, and light. In practical terms the UK categories differ in some respects from those agreed by ICAO. The parameters of the various categories are set by using the all-up weight of the aricraft expressed in kilograms.

## Wake Turbulence Categories in the United Kingdom

| | |
|---|---|
| More than 136,000 kg | Heavy |
| 40,000 kg to 136,000 kg | Medium |
| 17,000 kg to 40,000 kg | Small |
| 7,000 kg to 17,000 kg | Light |
| Less than 7,000 kg | Light |

## Examples of aircraft types, all-up weights, and UK/ICAO Wake Categories

| | | |
|---|---|---|
| A300 Airbus | 137,000 kg | Heavy |

| Boeing 747 | 353,000 kg | Heavy |
| Concorde | 181,000 kg | Heavy |
| Douglas DC 10 | 250,000 kg | Heavy |
| BAC–111 | 41,000 kg | Medium |
| Boeing 727 | 76,000 kg | Medium |
| Hercules | 80,000 kg | Medium |
| Learjet | 6,000 kg | Light |
| Islander | 3,600 kg | Light |
| Piper Navajo | 2,300 kg | Light |
| Fokker F 27 | 20,000 kg | Small (ICAO—Medium) |
| HS 748 | 22,000 kg | Small (ICAO—Medium |

The separation standards to be applied on final approach to give the required spacing for Wake Vortex purposes are:

| Leading aircraft | Aircraft following or crossing behind | Minimum distance | Time equivalent |
|---|---|---|---|
| Heavy | Heavy | 4 miles | 2 minutes |
| | Medium | 5 miles | 3 minutes |
| | Small | 6 miles | 3 minutes |
| | Light | 8 miles | 4 minutes |
| Medium | Heavy | (Normal ATC separation) | |
| | Medium | 3 miles | 2 minutes |
| | Small | 4 miles | 2 minutes |
| | Light | 6 miles | 3 minutes |
| Small | Heavy | (Normal ATC separation) | |
| | Medium or Small | 3 miles | 2 minutes |
| | Light | 4 miles | 2 minutes |

These same heavy category aircraft also create wake vortices on take-off and again a time restriction is applied to following aircraft. The minimum time is two minutes, with a time of three minutes if the second aircraft is in the small or light category.

This chapter began with the statement that an air traffic service is expected to provide a safe, orderly, and expeditious flow of air traffic. It should now be evident that no single element of that statement is to be enhanced at the expense of any other. The Air Traffic Controller is required to balance all three elements in a continuous exercise of fine judgement. This is not an easy skill to acquire but one which, nonetheless, is succesfully practised day in and day out.

**Chapter 6**

# Navigational aids

It is all very well to slice up the sky and to allocate names, colours and numbers to the component pieces. It is quite another matter to ensure that the aircraft which use it can stay inside the protection that it affords. In order that a pilot can find his way about and establish himself on a required track it is necessary to 'signpost' the route for him. This is done by a number of different radio guidance systems known as radio navigational aids. To be of any real value in the ATC system these aids must have a high order of reliability and accuracy.

The following navigational aids are all known as 'point source' aids. That is to say they provide information from a single source in the form of a ground station. They either transmit information continuously or can be interrogated by equipment carried in the aircraft. The information obtained enables the pilot to work out a position relative to the aid and the ease and accuracy with which this can be done will depend upon the type of aid being used and the instrument display in the cockpit. The principle radio navigational aids are as follows:

## The Non-directional Beacon (NDB)

This aid operates in the medium frequency band and has a maximum range of 50 or 100 miles depending upon its purpose. The shorter range NDB will be found in use within Terminal Control Areas and is used as the basis of a holding point or stack. The longer range version is used as an en-route aid. The NDB transmits continuously in all directions, rather like an ordinary radio station. To use this aid the pilot tunes in his receiver to the required frequency and a needle on the appropriate cockpit instrument will swing round to point at the aid. The face of the instrument is marked off in degrees with zero being at the top and representing the nose of the aircraft. By turning the aircraft so that the pointer goes around to the zero the pilot can aim the aircraft straight at the aid which represents a known point on the surface of the earth.

The use of a single NDB is, however, very limited in the information it provides. No indication is given of where the aircraft is now, or how far away from the NDB it is. To provide useful information it is necessary to use a second NDB simultaneously. With two known points identified as bearings it is possible to plot these on a map and the position of the aircraft is at the point ot intersection. All examples of this type of navigational aid also transmit their discreet identities in morse code so that they can be positively identified.

Although this was the main navigational aid in use in the airways

*DME (Distance Measuring Equipment) aerial array. Photograph by the author, courtesy of the CAA.)*

system for many years it has certain disadvantages in addition to those already mentioned. Operating in the frequency band it does, it is prone to interference and the aircraft receiver has a very poor rate of accuracy when the aircraft is flying in or near thunderstorms. Lightning flashes cause the needle to swing towards the discharge and in a heavy storm it is all but useless. There are still quite a number of NDBs in use in the United Kingdom and around the world but many have been replaced by other aids such as VOR or DVOR which, in addition to being less prone to interference, provide better accuracy and information to the pilot.

## Very High Frequency Omni-directional Range (VOR)

The next generation of radio navigational aid, the VOR transmission pattern is so arranged that the aid appears to transmit a number of straight lines, known as radials. By selecting the appropriate VOR frequency on the aircraft VHF receiver the pilot will have displayed in front of him a three digit figure which will identify which radial out of 360 he is on. The display also has two 'windows' which show either the word 'to' or 'from'. The purpose of this is to indicate to the pilot the radial he is on and whether following that radial will take him towards or away from the aid. Again, the use of two VOR facilities will enable the pilot to plot his position.

Less prone to interference than the NDB, the VOR has a range of 150 to 200 miles. Once again the information obtained, although more accurate, is limited. There is still no indication of range from the aid and the method of plotting aircraft positions on maps, certainly as far as the airliner is concerned, is somewhat old hat. It is necessary therefore to provide an indication of range so that a position can be obtained using a single VOR.

## Distance Measuring Equipment (DME)

This is the aid used in conjunction with VOR and very often the two aids are co-located. Selection of a VOR frequency will also select the appropriate and associated DME. The range of DME is about 200 miles. To use DME the aircraft needs to be fitted with a DME transmitter/receiver which is known as an interrogator. The equipment sends a signal to the DME and this is retransmitted to the aircraft receiver. As radio waves travel at a known speed, 186,000 miles per second, it is possible for the equipment to measure the time taken for the signal to leave the aircraft and return and to convert this into a distance expressed in miles. The distance or range will, of course, be a 'slant distance', because the aircraft will nearly always be well above the facility. An aircraft that is flying at an altitude of eight miles will never, on the DME display, appear to get closer to the aid than eight miles even when it is directly overhead. However, in practice, by this time the pilot will already be using another VOR/DME so that it is not really a problem. This aid provides the pilot with the missing information—the VOR indicates the radial and shows whether the aircraft is flying towards or away from the aid whilst the DME indicates range. The pilot is now aware of his exact position.

## Doppler Very High Frequency Omni-directional Range (DVOR)

The VOR, although more accurate and less prone to interference than the NDB, still suffers from the latter to a certain extent and difficult terrain can also cause difficulties with sitings. The principle is however a sound one and developments have enabled the introduction of the Doppler VOR. This uses the well known doppler principle to generate the ground signals and has removed most of the problems associated with NDB and VOR installations.

*Doppler VOR. The platform or counterpoise below the mushroom aerials acts as a reflective surface.* (Photograph by the author, courtesy of the CAA.)

From the pilot's viewpoint there is no difference in the basic information he can obtain from a DVOR. The cockpit display is just the same and the DVOR has of course, a co-located DME.

As has been said, all of these aids are 'point source' and by siting them in strategic positions it is possible to signpost the routes in the sky along which the aircraft are required to fly. Needless to say there is a drawback to this method. Provide a motorway between two major cities, encourage people to use it and, lo and behold, congestion. An airway is not dissimilar and by confining aircraft to a limited portion of the sky congestion will also arise from time to time.

## Area navigation aids

Prior to the beginning of World War 2 a considerable amount of research and development work into the properties and use of radio waves was undertaken both in this country and in Germany. Initially this work was concentrated, in the aviation field at least, on the provision of a radio beam guidance system for use in bad weather, at night and for 'blind landing'. With the outbreak of hostilities in 1939 this work went ahead at an unprecedented rate and the part played by radar in the defeat of the Luftwaffe is well documented.

Not so well known perhaps is the effort made to find a radio navigational aid which would enable aircraft not only to navigate in poor weather or at night but with a degree of accuracy sufficient to ensure a successful arrival over the intended target. Various aids such as Knickebein, Loran, Consul and Decca were developed and some of them were usable either by aircraft or ships. These aids use a number of ground stations which transmit a radio pattern into the air. By carefully arranging these transmissions it is possible, at the point of reception, to calculate differences in phase or frequency. Receivers and displays in the aircraft will enable the information to be interpreted in a form suitable for position finding. Because the properties and behaviour of these radio waves can be forecast it is also possible to draw charts for use in conjunction with the appropriate aid. This type of radio navigational aid is known as a hyperbolic navigation system and perhaps the best known of these is the Decca Navigator. Employing a combination of frequencies in the Low Frequency (LF) band it has a usable range of up to 240 miles. A further development of this system was the introduction of the Decca flight log. This log utilises a mechanically moved map with the aircraft being represented by a pen. This gives not only the current position of the aircraft but also shows the track history.

A system using a similar basic principle has been undergoing development for a number of years under the sponsorship of the United States Navy. Designed to give world-wide navigational coverage it employs radio transmissions at Very Low Frequency (VLF) which have the advantage of being usable at extremely long range. The system, known as OMEGA, requires eight transmitter sites only to give total global coverage. Undergoing installation at the time of writing these eight stations are being operated by Norway, Liberia, France, Argentina, Australia, Japan, and two by the United States, one in Hawaii and one in North Dakota. Again hyperbolic techniques are employed using the signals received from a number of ground stations. All of these concepts allow for area navigation and could, in theory at least, go some way towards relieving the most congested routes. Even though an aircraft fitted with one of these systems can accurately fly a given route the practical value to ATC is limited at this time. To be generally adopted all of the participating aircraft would need to have the ability to navigate to the same standard.

There is always one basic problem in the provision of a navigational aid by external sources such as point source aids, they have to be available in the first place, otherwise all that expensive airborne equipment is carried as so much dead weight. There are parts of the world, not all of them by any means remote, where by reason of economics or terrain features the availability and serviceability of ground based aids is less than desirable. As a result more than one well equipped aircraft has become little more than a black mark on a mountain side.

Aviation has sometimes developed ideas which had applications in areas other than flying, likewise the aviation industry can sometimes make use of equipment or methods not originally intended for its specific use. In the military field, and also in the space programme, much research has been done to devise an aid to navigation which was completely self-contained. In these days of electronic wizardry it is necessary for say, a submarine or an attacking aircraft, to be able to fix its position without at the same time announcing its presence to anyone who cares to listen on the appropriate frequency. Similarly the space programme needed a device to fix positions when the space craft was many miles from earth. The system devised is known as inertial guidance, the first operational form of which appeared in the German V2 rocket during World War 2. Its development and application for general and practical use was not fully realised until suitably compact digital computers also became available.

This system makes use of the properties of a gyroscope. When made to spin rapidly it will balance in all sorts of attitudes and resist any attempt to change them. What, in fact, it does is to maintain a position in space rather than one relative to the earth. Three extremely accurate gyros are mounted on a 'platform' in the aircraft which is so mounted that it can move freely in any and every direction. To this gyroscopically controlled reference table are attached accelerometers which will sense any movement. If the initial position and heading of the aircraft is entered into the inertial navigation equipment any subsequent movement of the aircraft will be sensed by the accelerometers. These then send signals to the on-board computer which does the necessary mathematics to enable the present position of the aircraft to be calculated and displayed. Position information can be displayed in a number of ways including latitude and longitude, as a position on rolling map or a bearing and distance.

In aviation the inertial guidance system is very useful to the civilian pilot especially in long over water trips or in areas where conventional ground based aids are few and far between. Possessing all the advantages of a self contained system it has the disadvantage of being very expensive. In spite of this it is steadily being adopted by many of the world's airlines and satisfies the requirement for an area navigation system. From an ATC point of view its adoption is not yet sufficiently general to warrant any far reaching change within the current airways system. Inertial guidance can also be used in conjunction with the more conventional methods of navigation where these exist.

Although it is not an en-route navigational aid one more point source type of aid remains to be discussed. To be truly accurate it is a guidance system from two point sources.

## The Instrument Landing System (ILS)

The ILS is a ground based radio landing aid which enables a pilot to line up on the extended centreline of the landing runway and at the same time to maintain terrain clearance. The aid is pilot interpreted from an instrument in the cockpit. The ILS consists of four major components.

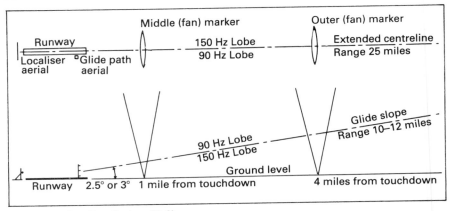

*Instrument Landing System (ILS).*

## The localiser
The localiser aerial array is sited at the far end of the landing runway and transmits two intersecting radio beams along the extended centre line of that runway. It has a range of approximately 25 miles and it provides guidance to fly left or right to capture and maintain the extended centreline.

## The glide path
The glide path aerial array is sited adjacent to the touchdown point of the landing runway and is off-set to one side. Again, it transmits two intersecting radio beams which provide guidance to fly up or down. The glide slope beam is so arranged that it gives automatic terrain clearance and a constant descent path over a range of some 10 to 12 miles. In the UK the angle of the glide slope is either 2.5° or 3° depending upon the terrain clearance required.

## Marker beacons
The marker beacon is designed to indicate to the pilot of a landing aircraft his position along the beams in relation to the touch down point. These beacons transmit a restricted beam vertically through the guidance beams in a shape like a lady's fan which explains the alternative name of fan markers sometimes given to beacons of this type. Originally the system employed three of these markers sited at 1,000–1,500 ft, 3,500 ft and four miles from touchdown. As the aircraft passes over these markers both audio and visual signals are received. The pilot will hear on his headset a low tone of two Morse

dashes per second and at the same time a purple light flashes in sequence. This indicates to the pilot that the aircraft is passing over the outer marker. As the middle marker is passed he will hear a medium tone in Morse of dash-dot-dash per second and an amber light will flash. Lastly, he will hear a high pitched tone of six Morse dots per second and a white light will flash as the aircraft passes over the inner marker. Some ILS installations do not now include the inner marker.

## Aircraft equipment

The aircraft carries aerials to receive both the glide slope and the centreline guidance signals. The information received is then displayed on the single instrument provided for this purpose in the cockpit. A horizontal needle indicates the relative position of the desired glide slope whilst a vertical needle indicates the relative position of the desired centreline. In the event of any failure of the ground equipment or of the equipment on the aircraft a 'flag' showing the word 'off' will appear at the apporopriate needle. Any

*ILS localiser and glide path aerials. Unlike an operational system both aerials are sited together at the College of Telecommunications Engineering for the convenience of technical training. (Photograph by the author, courtesy of the CAA.)*

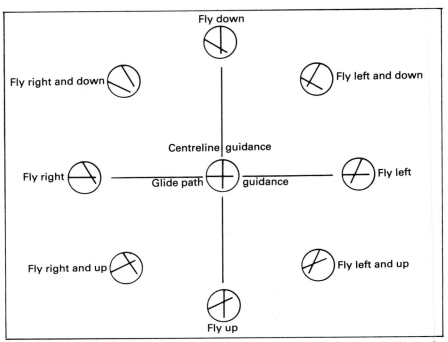

ILS cockpit indications. The aircraft is always flown towards the needle to obtain the correct indications as shown in the centre of the diagram. These indicate that it is on the extended centreline of the runway and on the glide slope. At this point the pilot will report that he is 'established' on the ILS.

further indications from that needle must then be ignored or approach discontinued.

In 1949 the ILS system was adopted as the standard approach and landing aid. Subsequent development led to an increase in its integrity and reliability, allowing for an increase in its versatility. As a result a number of categories have been introduced to indicate the limits of use of any particular ILS installation. These are: *Category 1* —Usable with a minimum cloud base of 60 m and a runway visibility of not less than 800 m; *Category 2*—Usable with a minimum cloud base of 30 m and a runway visibility of not less than 400 m; and *Category 3*—Usable with the cloud base at zero and in zero visibility.

Guidance is also available along the runway centreline and all four main approaches to London (Heathrow) are equipped with Category 3 ILS. Because of the complete reliance placed upon the system by the pilot each ILS is checked for operational integrity by a flight check every month, carried out by a specially equipped aircraft of the CAA's Flying Unit. The total system is also re-calibrated annually.

ILS as a system is not however without its problems. It can only be installed where the surrounding terrain permits uninterrupted transmission of its signals. Also, because it relies upon part of those transmissions being reflected by the ground in front of the aerials it can be adversely affected by any change in those reflective properties, for example when snow is present.

A pilot may fly the ILS system manually by direct reference to the cockpit instrument needles or he may elect, in a suitably equipped aircraft, to fly a 'coupled' approach. The latter couples the ILS signals to the auto-pilot so that in effect the aircraft makes its own adjustments to maintain the glide slope and centreline, with the pilot monitoring the system and completing the flare or round out for a visual landing. The logical development of this was for the aircraft system to control the aircraft all the way onto the runway. Technically this was possible but for some time the reliable and accurate carrying out of the round out proved to be the sticking point. This problem was, however, overcome and fully controlled 'auto-land' approaches are now commonplace and make for more efficient operation with less diversions and passenger aggravation. As an additional safety factor however airlines will also specify a set of minimum figures below which an approach of this type may not be attempted.

Although in general use and adequate at most airfields the ILS system is in principle almost 35 years old and it was realised that a replacement system was needed. ICAO published an operational requirement in 1972 for a new non-visual approach and landing aid. A better understanding of the use of microwaves meant that the difficulties of terrain could be overcome and so evolved the Micro-wave Landing System (MLS). However because of the heavy financial investment already made in both ground and airborne ILS equipment around the world the ILS system gained protection until 1995.

ICAO, under its Air Navigation Commission set up an All Weather Operations Panel to evaluate and oversee the develop-ment of an MLS system, a number of which were undergoing development in various parts of the world. The four major con-tenders were Australia and the USA with a system based upon a

Time Reference Scanning Beam (TRSB), and the UK with a system based upon Doppler MLS and the Federal Republic of Germany with a DME based system. The choice was finally narrowed to a TRSB system or a Doppler MLS one and the outcome was a recommendation to adopt as standard the system based upon TRSB.

Like ILS the MLS system provides guidance in azimuth and elevation, the important difference is that unlike ILS this guidance information is available 40° either side of the extended centreline of

*The Microwave Landing System (MLS). Unlike the Instrument Landing System, the Microwave Landing System provides azimuth and elevation guidance over a large area. Similar guidance information is also available to an aircraft carrying out a missed approach.*

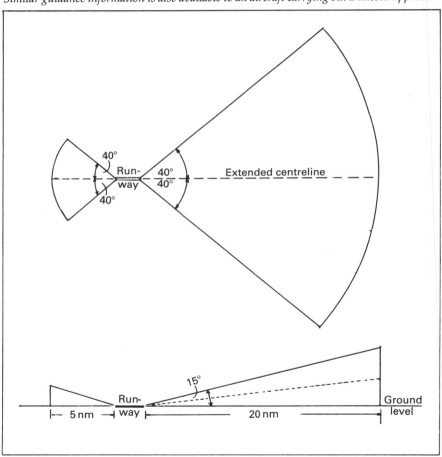

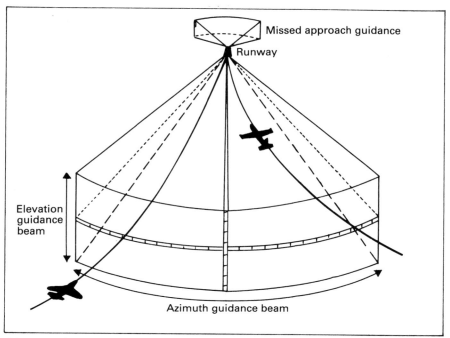

Missed approach guidance

Runway

Elevation
guidance
beam

Azimuth guidance beam

*Diagram showing how the Microwave Landing System provides guidance on multiple flightpaths, so increasing the capacity of the system.*

the runway. In theory at least it should be possible to increase the landing rate as it will not be necessary for all aircraft to be positioned into an orderly queue and placed exactly onto a single guidance beam. However this facility will need much further work before general adoption and such a radical departure from the norm cannot simply be introduced overnight. It also has to be borne in mind that aircraft already carry highly sophisticated landing aids and their operators do not take kindly to having these declared redundant. Wherever possible any replacement aid should be usable by the airborne equipment already in existence. Research would indicate that the incoming MLS signals will be capable of being used through the standard ILS cockpit display.

**Chapter 7**

# The CAA support organisations

It will be appreciated that the CAA and NATS employ a great many people with specialist and technical skills. Furthermore, on the ATC side at least, they are not the skills that can be garnered from other employers or outside industries. In the immediate post-war years of ATC by far the majority of staff came from the armed forces with the greatest number coming, not unnaturally, from the Royal Air Force and a few from the Fleet Air Arm. It is no mark of disrespect to say that at this time nobody had any clear idea as to what was really required of the embryo system and it grew for a while after the fashion of 'Topsy'. On the contrary it says much for the high standard of professionalism that any system was developed at all. Housed in ex-wartime buildings, using ex-wartime equipment, and controlling ex-wartime aircraft the system gradually evolved into a

*The CAA College of Air Traffic Control.* (Photograph by the author, courtesy of the CAA.)

true civil air traffic service. As time went by ATC began to acquire equipment and accommodation designed for and specific to its needs and the days when everything was either 'begged, borrowed or stolen' began to recede. As the ATC system began to evolve the need for training and support services became more apparent and so it was that a number of specialist and training establishments were founded.

The College of Air Traffic Control was formed, initially as the School of Air Traffic Control, adjacent to the airfield at Bournemouth (Hurn) Airport. Being close to a seaside town with plenty of accommodation available the college is non-residential and provides training in all aspects of ATC. Equipped with a range of simulators, both radar and non-radar training is given by means of classroom lectures, films, video and practical simulator work in Aerodrome, Approach and Area Control. Students are examined orally, in writing and practically at set stages in their training and are, in addition, required to undergo periods of practical training in the field. This is to prove that they can apply the training received in a real life situation. During field training and because they are dealing with 'live' traffic they are at all times working under the close supervision of a trained controller. During their course they also undertake a limited amount of flying training.

Both Air Traffic Controllers and Air Traffic Control Assistants are

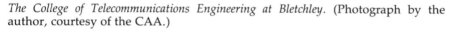

*The College of Telecommunications Engineering at Bletchley.* (Photograph by the author, courtesy of the CAA.)

required to have and maintain a level of physical fitness and the controllers undergo an annual medical check to ensure that there is no falling off from this standard.

Successful students leave the College to work in the field in possession of an Air Traffic Controllers License. This however is not the end of the road, onto that license must go various validations and ratings. That is to say he or she, ATC is not solely a man's prerogative, must prove their practical ability at the air traffic service unit to which they are posted. If for any reason a controller fails to practice his particular skills for a period exceeding 90 days then his local qualifications become invalid and he or she has to repeat the process all over again. This ensures that as far as possible those who practice the art of ATC are thoroughly conversant with the system.

In addition to these courses the College also provides refresher training as well as courses in data processing, technical appreciation and instructor training. Although a high percentage of the through-put of the College is for the benefit of the CAA, including an ATCO Cadet scheme, staff are also trained for work at UK airfields where the CAA does not provide the controlling authority and training is given to a substantial number of students from overseas every year.

Technical training needs are met by the College of Telecommunications Engineering established originally as the Civil Aviation Signals Training Establishment. Situated within the grounds of Bletchley Park, courses are offered in a whole range of technical subjects both to CAA staff and to students from many countries overseas. These courses are divided into five main groups—radar, navigational aids, communications equipment, computers and processing equipment, and a cadet training scheme. Unlike the College at Hurn, residential accommodation for up to 100 students is available.

A large part of the College site consists of a $7\frac{1}{4}$ acre field on which are situated a number of non-operational landing and radar aids similar to those in every day use. Because of their non-operational mode they can be stripped down for long periods to reveal their innermost workings and fault finding techniques can be practised. Again the training is carried out by classroom teaching, practical demonstration and by allowing the student a considerable amount of 'hands on' familiarisation. Staff are trained for employment at CAA airports, control centres, communications centres, radar stations and its own maintenance and repair organisation.

As well as the two major training Colleges the CAA operates

*The CAA Evaluation Unit.* (Photograph by the author, courtesy of the CAA.)

three support units. The first of these is the Telecommunications Engineering Establishment based at Gatwick from where a wide range of engineering support services are provided. Field and laboratory engineering trials and evaluations are carried out as well as the repair and maintenance of major telecommunications equipment. Installation and acceptance testing of equipment and the design and manufacture of specialist equipment is also undertaken.

The second support unit is once again at Bournemouth (Hurn) Airport and is co-located with the College of Air Traffic Control. The Air Traffic Control Evaluation Unit evaluates proposed Air Traffic Control techniques, systems and specialised equipments. It is able to mount complex simulations in both real and fast time using sophisticated computer driven simulator systems. Large numbers of aircraft can be 'flown' on the radar simulators and in this way it is possible to test new procedures and the organisation required to deal with them.

The third support organisation is the Civil Aviation Authority Flying Unit based at Stansted Airport. It is part of the overall safety system to check and calibrate the various en-route and airport navigational aids and to this end CAAFU possesses a small number of aircraft of its own specially fitted out with flight test equipment for this work. In addition, when an accident occurs and there is reason to believe that a particular navigational aid or landing aid was contributory to that accident, the aid will be withdrawn from service until such time as it can be checked by a CAAFU aircraft and its integrity proved. Then and only then will it be released for normal service.

The foregoing is but a glimpse of the work which is carried out to support and maintain the Air Traffic Control service. Although these organisations do not figure prominently in the public eye they are nonetheless highly respected within the aviation world and their level of expertise and professionalism is held in high regard by many overseas organisations who avail themselves of the facilities offered from time to time.

The Air Traffic Controller is not, of course, able to ply his particular trade free from interference or without consideration for others. It would indeed be a perfect world where the sun always shone, the aircraft were always on time, and the wind always blew fair. He has to co-operate and co-ordinate his efforts with a number of related bodies and be flexible enough to adapt his application of the ATC system to allow for conditions and restrictions imposed from outside.

One such outside pressure is the commercial airline. At the end of the day the owning airliner operator expects to make an operating profit. Aircraft sitting on the ground do not make money, while an aircraft kept in the air unnecessarily will eat into the profit margins. Fuel is very expensive and the fitting, either new or retrospectively, of more economical engines only goes part of the way to providing an acceptable profit margin.

Another consideration at most major airports, and increasingly at many smaller ones, is the influence of public opinion which has often been of sufficient weight to impose restrictions on routeings and power settings immediately after take-off and in some cases, on the approach path too. These 'noise abatement' procedures are strictly enforced and transgressors can and do face disciplinary action and heavy fines. From the point of view of ATC they can also cause additional problems, slowing down the rate at which traffic can be moved.

The controller must also be mindful of operating restrictions placed on certain types of aircraft during particular phases of flight.

A useful device is to clear aircraft onto a runway for an immediate or rolling take-off. By adopting a running start runway occupancy time is reduced and will often enable an aircraft to get away when there is also a stream of inbound traffic. There is, however, at least one well known type of three engined airliner where the pilot will always come to a full stop before applying full power and commencing the take-off roll. This is because the centre tail mounted engine does not really like being opened up to full power too quickly and if attempted may well 'flame-out', causing the take-off to be abandoned at a most inconvenient time.

There are also restrictions on airspeed to be considered. An aircraft is designed to push its way through the air with the minimum of resistance but the relationship between minimum safe flying speed and maximum flying speed may be quite close on some aircraft types and well separated on others. A visit to a major flying display will sometimes show airliners both large and small being handled like some sort of improbable fighter. The point to appreciate however is that the pilot knows beforehand what he intends to do and sets his aircraft up accordingly. In normal airline operation quite high rates of descent can be achieved of some 7–10,000 ft per minute if the aircraft is in the proper configuration at the appropriate airspeed. The fare paying passenger, rightly, does not take kindly to being thrown around the sky or to sudden changes in altitude or speed. The controller therefore has to organise his separation moves and routeings to ensure a smooth passage and comfortable rate of descent. Many Terminal Control Areas are now subjected to speed restrictions. The application of these restrictions has the advantage from the ATC viewpoint of reducing the various types of aircraft involved to something nearer what might be termed a 'standard' aircraft. This eases the overall handling problem without any significant increase in overall delay.

By and large within the UK FIR boundaries the weather does not play an overly significant part. True there are generally predictable periods of the year when fog, snow, ice and thunderstorms do cause disruption to the smooth flow of traffic, but that applies in equal measure to other forms of transport too. Snow causes immediate and almost total chaos but fortunately seldom lasts over long and can be cleared away. Ice on runways and taxyways can be gritted and operations continued. Fog can be more persistent and can cause disruption but this is being slowly overcome by equipping airfields and aircraft with landing aids of sufficient accuracy and reliability to enable operations to continue in all but the very worst visibility. Although this is a very expensive solution it has to be balanced against an operator finding the bulk of his fleet fogged in for two or three days.

Of all the weather phenomena the least understood and therefore the most potentially dangerous is the thunderstorm. The Air Traffic Controller has to rely heavily on pilot reports as he is the person closest to the weather and the first to feel directly its effect. Very big thunderstorms will often show on radar but the danger is that if the Radar Controller tries to steer an aircraft around a major storm he may well point it straight at a smaller one. The terms small and large are of course only relative, a lightning strike or a battering from hailstones is equally unpleasant no matter the size of storm from which they originate.

Nearly all airliners and many of the executive and business aircraft carry a nose mounted weather radar. This can have a range of up to 30 miles and is of high definition, scanning a fan shaped area ahead of the aircraft's line of flight. On approaching bad weather of this type a pilot will often request a change of heading to avoid the worst of the storm and ATC will, whenever possible, grant the request. A thunderstorm overhead or very close to an airfield will often cause sudden and dramatic changes in wind speed and direction, causing the need to change the operating runway with the consequent disruption to the flow of traffic approaching the airfield.

Thunderstorms originate in a type of cloud known as Cumulo-Nimbus and are described as being of great vertical extent. In plain language this can mean that they have a base of around 1,000 ft and go all the way up to 40,000 ft. Fortunately storms of this size are not an everyday occurrence in the United Kingdom. These cloud formations also contain rapidly moving columns of air, some vertically upwards, some vertically downwards, and not necessarily very far apart. It has not been unknown for an aircraft to be totally destroyed in the air by flying into one of these clouds. The active thunderstorm is a nasty beast and one of those in a TMA or in the middle of an airway can play havoc with what was designed to be a nice orderly system.

Many parts of the world are subject to seasonal variations in air traffic movement rates. As far as the UK is concerned this occurs because of the massive popularity of Spain as a holiday destination. From roughly the Easter weekend onwards until September the

Spanish mainland and in particular the island of Majorca is subjected to a veritable bombardment of 'inclusive tour' traffic. This traffic is generated not only within the United Kingdom but also from our European neighbours. Such peak traffic seriously overloads the capacity of the ATC system at the Spanish end and produces a knock-on effect right back down the line to the airfields of departure. At such times to maintain a safe flow of traffic (not to mention the sanity of the Spanish Air Traffic Controllers) a system known as Flow Control is introduced. This is designed to restrict the number of aircraft arriving together at the destination end. Flying times are calculated back down the route to eventually arrive at a preferred take-off time known as a slot.

To co-ordinate the United Kingdom's input into the general flow a Departure Flow Regulator position is established at the London Air Traffic Control Centre at West Drayton. The Flow Controller has his information constantly updated and accepts bids from UK airfields with traffic to offer and relates this to his total allocation of slots. He then offers back slot times to the airfields and sets his pattern generally on an hourly basis. Thus a typical allocation in any hour might be; two departures from Gatwick, one from Heathrow, and one each from Birmingham, Manchester, Stansted and Glasgow. In the next hour other airfields such as Teeside, Belfast or Cardiff would be offered slots in turn. Inevitably this leads to frustrating delays on the ground and an understandable reaction on the part of the airlines to get their passengers through the formalities and into the departure lounges as quickly as possible. Occasionally a further frustrating delay will occur when a passenger discovers that his or her passport has been packed in the luggage presently being stowed safely away in the hold of the aircraft. As a result a slot can be lost and if this occurs close to departure time it cannot even be offered to another airfield and is lost completely. Frustration all round, and not always the fault of ATC.

These are just a selection of the additional problems with which an Air Traffic Controller has to contend in order to carry out his own duties and meet the demands of others. Naturally these external pressures cannot ever be allowed to deflect the controller from his primary task of controlling aircraft in a safe and orderly manner.

**Chapter 8**

# ATC—the parts of the system

To the casual observer the most obvious sign of the presence of Air Traffic Control is the structure commonly known as the Control Tower. This heavily glazed structure is more correctly called the Visual Control Room or VCR, and is also known in the United States as the Cab. Although the function of all VCRs is essentially the same the design and location may differ markedly. A number of airfields still retain structures of wartime vintage whilst others, such as London (Gatwick), sport the very latest in stalk mounted VCRs. Whatever their shape or origin the basic function of the VCR remains the same, to give an overall and all round view of the airfield surface, the traffic upon it, and arriving and departing traffic within a radius of a few miles. In practice however this ideal is not always realised. Some airfields have been expanded considerably over the years, and sometimes this expansion has been all in one direction. This can be dictated by the presence of a well established housing estate, a railway line or river so that the occupants of the VCR are literally situated at one end of the airfield.

The function of the VCR is to exercise control over the airfield, its approaches, aprons and taxyways. Staffing will vary considerably depending upon the amount of traffic handled and the hours of operation of the particular airfield. However, the size of the operation makes no difference to the qualifications of those employed there, the VCR controller being properly trained, licensed and validated to work in that particular location. At busier airfields there will be additional staff to handle the increased workload and air-

**Right** *The operations capsule at the top of the control tower at Gatwick airport. The accommodation consists of a Visual Control Room on the top floor from which Air Traffic Officers enjoy an uninterrupted 360° view over the runways and taxyways, a middle floor containing telecommunications equipment and a lower floor which includes rest rooms and an air conditioning plant. (CAA)*

**Left** *The control tower at Heathrow airport with ASMI radar in the housing alongside the VCR. (CAA)*

**Below** *The control tower complex at Bournemouth (Hurn) airport with the radio mast on the left.*

fields that operate around the clock will staff its facilities on a shift basis.

The equipment fitted will also vary considerably between different airfields although certain basic items will be common to them all. The VCR controller will have to hand a telephone keyboard with some lines giving direct access to some other parts of the ATC system. A panel of radio telephony channels will be present, also a clock showing GMT, a display of flight progress strips and two dials, one showing wind speed and the other wind direction. A lighting control panel allows for the selection of runway, approach, or taxiway lighting as required. Lastly, the basic equipment may also include an Aldis lamp for signalling to non-radio aircraft and vehicles, and a pair of Very pistols for firing coloured flares. The latter will only be available where it is safe to fire into an open area. As most modern VCRs are situated amongst the terminal buildings the firing of flares is considered something less than desirable.

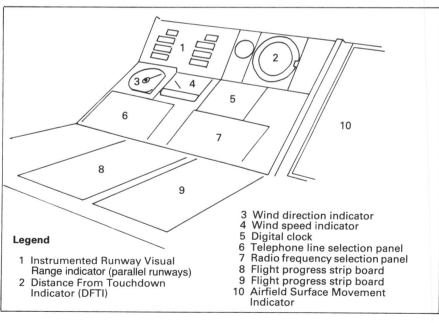

**Legend**

1 Instrumented Runway Visual Range indicator (parallel runways)
2 Distance From Touchdown Indicator (DFTI)
3 Wind direction indicator
4 Wind speed indicator
5 Digital clock
6 Telephone line selection panel
7 Radio frequency selection panel
8 Flight progress strip board
9 Flight progress strip board
10 Airfield Surface Movement Indicator

At the larger and busier airfields the VCR controller will be able to avail himself of additional facilities such as a radar display. Whilst it is not usual for Radar Control to be conducted from the VCR it is useful for the controller to be able to check where any inbound traffic is on the approach, especially when the visibility is poor. It is a particularly useful device when the inbound and outbound traffic flow is at a peak and enables a single runway to be utilised to the full.

The radar display may well be a simple 'repeater' showing the same radar picture as is available to the Approach Radar Controller. However as the need for radar information is limited and of essential interest only on the approach path, some VCRs are equipped with a type of radar display known as a Distance From Touchdown Indicator (DFTI). This small display utilises the information gained when the main radar aerial is pointing along the approach path but only displays the last ten miles.

Where an airfield is both large in surface area and constantly very busy another radar device may be available to the VCR controller. This short range, high definition radar shows the whole of the airfield surface in some detail and anything moving upon that surface, be it aircraft or vehicle. Known as the Airfield Surface Movement Indicator or ASMI the aerial revolves at a higher speed than the four to six revolutions per minute of the longer range search radar. Two such installations exist in the United Kingdom, one at London (Heathrow) and the other, recently installed, at London (Gatwick). The combination of a high aerial turning rate and the short range results in a display more akin to a television picture. This aid is extremely useful when controlling aircraft and or vehicles in poor visibility or at night. The personnel and equipment described collectively form an aerodrome control unit responsible for providing the following services; Aerodrome Control service, Flight Information Service and alerting service.

Aerodrome Control is responsible for issuing information and instructions to aircraft under its control and to assist pilots in preventing collisions between aircraft in the air, taking off and landing, moving on the apron or taxyways and between aircraft and vehicles, obstructions and other aircraft on the manoeuvring area. This responsibility may be vested in a single controller in the VCR

**Left** *The control desk of the Air Departures Controller in the Visual Control Room of the control tower at Heathrow airport.* (Photograph courtesy of the CAA.)

*Inside the Visual Control Room at the top of the control tower at Gatwick airport. In the centre foreground is one of the ground movement radar displays adjacent to the airfield lighting control panel. (CAA).*

but again where the traffic loading is high it may be divided between the Air Controller and a Ground Movements Controller. In this case the Air Controller is responsible for those airborne aircraft under his control including those taking off and just about to land and has absolute authority over all movements on active runways and their access points. The Ground Movements Controller (GMC) is responsible for aircraft movement on the apron, vehicles and other aircraft on the manoeuvring area. The GMC position may also be used to read out airways clearances to departing aircraft. The division of responsibility is made necessary by the need to keep under control the number and length of radio telephony transmissions made from a single source thus helping to keep the traffic moving freely.

No individual part of the air traffic service is designed or required to stand alone and the VCR controller is required to liaise closely with Approach Control to carry out co-ordination of arriving flights and with the Air Traffic Control Centre for departures. Such co-

*The control desk of the Ground Movements Controller in the Visual Control Room at Heathrow airport. (CAA.)*

ordination is vital if a smooth flow of air traffic is to be achieved. It should not be assumed that the essentially visual nature of VCR work makes the job any easier. The controllers be they air or ground have a great deal to do, to watch and remember. There are, in addition to the aircraft, many vehicles which go about their lawful occasions; the surface of the airfield has to be inspected at regular intervals and the large expanses of grass have to be cut regularly. Various landing aids, navigational aids and airfield lighting have to be inspected and maintained regularly.

As air traffic has steadily increased ways have had to be found to reduce the controller workload, in particular the amount of time spent using the radio telephone. One answer came in the form of an automatic transmission of certain basic airfield information, known as the Automatic Terminal Information Service or ATIS. By tuning to a published frequency the pilot is able to obtain information on which runway is in use, the direction and speed of the wind, the aerodrome QFE and the QNH, the air temperature and dewpoint and any other essential information, all of this by automatic broadcast. He will also pick up details on any unserviceable departure navigational aids, special weather reports and any other information considered to be of use. These automatic transmissions are coded with the first of the day being 'ALPHA' and so on alphabetically. As new or revised messages are put onto the system so the next letter is allocated. Prior to the adoption of this system a controller was required to transmit the information to each and every aircraft.

A second method adopted to reduce the R/T workload was the introduction of Standard Instrument Departures of SIDs. As most commercial aircraft travel along well designated routes it is possible to standardise the departure clearances so that the pilot, having been given the title of his departure SID refers to a document carried in the aircraft for the details. This will show a pictorial representation of the route, any noise abatement restrictions, beacons to be crossed and at what height, and the radio frequency to be used after take-off. At the airfields where the SID system is in use a major reduction in R/T occupancy time has resulted. For example, prior to the introduction of SIDs a quite routine flight from Manchester to the Isle of Man, departing runway 24 would have entailed the reading of a full clearance and a 'read back' by the aircraft, all done as the aircraft taxyed out to the holding point. The exchange being as follows:

*ATC*: Golf Yankee Sierra I have your airways clearance when ready.

*Aircraft*: Golf Yankee Sierra, roger, go ahead.

*ATC*: Golf Alpha Oscar Yankee Sierra is cleared via Whitegate, Wallasey, Red Three (Airway) to the Isle of Man. To cross Whitegate three thousand five hundred feet, Wallasey three thousand five hundred feet, to climb, when instructed by radar from three thousand five hundred feet to Flight Level one two zero and maintain.

*Aircraft*: Roger, Yankee Sierra is cleared Red Three to the Isle of Man—Whitegate three five, Wallasey three five, to climb under radar from three five to one two zero to maintain.

*ATC*: Golf Yankee Sierra correct, clear to line up and report ready for take-off.

Not perhaps a very long exchange between controller and aircraft but when put into the context of over 150 movements a day it can be appreciated that something less wasteful of time was required. Under the SID system the same clearance would be identified as an 'Isle of Man 1 R'. By reference to the appropriate document the pilot would see that he was required to climb straight ahead after take-off to Whitegate to cross at 3,500 ft, then turn right onto a magnetic track of 312° which is also the 132° radial TO the Wallasey VOR to be crossed at 4,000 ft. At Wallasey, ahead on the 313° radial FROM the VOR to the Isle of Man. His airways frequency will be 125.1mHz on which he will be given instructions to climb further.

At the beginning of this chapter it was stated that one of the responsibilities of the VCR staff was to operate an 'alerting service'. This is not however vested solely in the VCR. The alerting service is available to all aircraft operating within UK Flight Information Regions and whose operation is known by the air traffic services. The responsibility for initiating search and rescue action normally rests with the air traffic service unit which was last in communication with the aircraft or is notified from an outside source.

Many readers will probably be familiar with the existence of special radio frequencies for use in acquiring help during an emergency. They are 121.5mHz (VHF) and 243mHz (UHF). However, it is a common misconception that any aircraft in emergency will automatically change to one of those frequencies. This is not so and, when thought about, is only common sense. Why leave a frequency where the aircraft type, height, position, routeing and destination are already known only to have to explain the whole thing all over again, and all this with an emergency to handle as well? The two frequencies mentioned are most often used by aircraft flying off airways or not under positive control. A frequency change may however be made once the degree of emergency has been ascertained to relieve R/T congestion so that the aircraft in emergency can receive undivided attention.

There are a number of 'triggers' for initiating the alerting service. Some of them are obvious such as when an aircraft is actually seen to crash or the pilot reports that he is about to crash. The radar returns may disappear from the radar screen and no radio contact can be made. The police or a member of the public may report a crash by telephone. Fortunately the number of emergencies that end in crashes is actually very few but they are treated as if this might be the end result. It is far better to be prepared for something which might not happen than be caught out when it does and the time to react will be measured in minutes.

When a pilot declares an emergency he will, given the opportunity, describe the nature of the problem and his immediate and long term intentions. He may wish to divert to an airfield close at hand or to return to the airfield of departure, especially if by doing so he can obtain immediate engineering assistance. Aircraft can always take-off at a weight heavier than that at which they can land so that it may be necessary to burn off or dump fuel before a landing can be attempted. Although the methods for dealing with emergencies are well laid out each one has to be treated individually as it occurs so that at the time of the actual event the Air Traffic Controller has to be able to assess quickly the type of problem involved and the assistance he can offer.

A four-engined aircraft which carries out a precautionary shut down of a single engine due to say falling oil pressure will normally be able to continue to destination at a somewhat reduced airspeed, especially if no long over-water legs are involved. Nonetheless, the emergency procedures at the airfield of arrival will be initiated because it might not end there. The engine problem may be mis-identified and the falling oil pressure a symptom rather than the sole problem. What if other engines have to be shut down? A study of aircraft accident reports will reveal that explosion and mid-air collision apart, nearly all begin with a relatively simple fault giving rise to a series of ever more serious failures until the situation passes beyond recovery.

It is then, the responsibility of any air traffic service unit to give assistance when required to any aircraft under its jurisdiction. As well as the laid down general procedures each air traffic service unit will also have readily available information which takes account of local requirements. These instructions are brief and concise and are usually available in the form of 'snatch boards' whose existence and location is known to everyone on duty. A sudden accident can be dealt with quickly and efficiently and in the correct order of priority without the people involved having to try and remember what to do next at a time when the workload is already high.

Not so obvious to the outside observer is the existence of another part of the ATC system—Approach Control. Often situated within the same building as the VCR the Approach Control unit may also be combined with an Approach Radar unit, an Aerodrome Control unit or a Zone Control unit. The Approach Control unit shall provide; Approach Control service, Flight Information Service and alerting service.

At aerodromes with controlled and special rules airspace, separation will be provided between IFR flights and between them and VFR flights. The areas of responsibility of Approach Control will again vary according to exact location but briefly it will provide an ATC service to aircraft released by Area Control until control is transferred to Aerodrome Control, to aircraft approaching from outside controlled airspace or special rules airspace, until control is transferred to Aerodrome Control and may also provide a service to departing aircraft until they are transferred to Area Control or they are clear of controlled or special rules airspace. They may also provide a service to aircraft overflying within the relevent airspace.

Outside of controlled or special rules airspace the situation is different as there is no legal requirement for aircraft flying outside of an Aerodrome Traffic Zone, controlled or special rules airspace to comply with ATC instructions as the service is advisory only. However, unless they indicate to the contrary pilots will be assumed to be complying with any ATC instructions.

Standard separation shall be provided between IFR flights from the time and place at which they are released by Area Control until such time as control is transferred to Aerodrome Control. The same applies to flights arriving from outside controlled or special rules airspace that place themselves under Approach Control. A similar service is given to departing aircraft taken over from Aerodrome Control until they are transferred to Area Control or they no longer wish to avail themselves of the service or are ten minutes flying time away from the aerodrome, whichever is the sooner. Aircraft which are overflying may place themselves under Approach Control until they are clear of the approach pattern and either no longer wish to avail themselves of the service or are ten minutes flying time away from the aerodrome, whichever is the sooner.

In many cases Approach Control will be combined with an Approach Radar unit. The area within which services can be provided is determined initially by the radar coverage of the equipment concerned but is, in any case, subject to an overall limit of 40 miles from the Aerodrome Traffic Zone. The Approach Radar unit provides a radar control service for flights within controlled or special rules airspace and a radar advisory service for flights outside of these. Additional services may also be provided in the form of surveillance radar approaches, radar vectoring and sequencing for ILS approaches, radar monitoring of ILS approaches and the control of departing and overflying aircraft.

Within each FIR an air traffic service unit is established to provide Area Control and is known as an Air Traffic Control Centre. The service provided by an ATCC is as follows; Area Control service, Flight Information Service and alerting service. The ATCC provides these services to aircraft which are departing from, arriving at, or are in transit, to the vicinity of an airport and which are outside the area of the air traffic services provided by them. In controlled and special rules airspace aircraft are provided with an ATC service, (with and without radar), and a Flight Information Service and aircraft are required to comply with ATC instructions. In advisory airspace, an ATC advisory service is provided, (with and without radar), and a Flight Information Service. Outside controlled, special rules, and advisory airspace, a radar advisory service is available where suitable radar coverage exists, and a Flight Information Service including proximity warnings. The latter are used to warn aircraft flying in the non-controlled airspace areas of the FIR of the existence, where known, of other aircraft in the vicinity. It is not possible to attempt positive control as there might well be yet other unknown aircraft and controlled avoidance of one conflict might lead to another. The principle of 'see and be seen' operates very much here.

In the United Kingdom Area Control services are provided from the ATCCs and sub-ATCCs, Joint (civil/military) ATC Radar Units, and the Oceanic Area Control Centre. The London Air Traffic Control Centre (LATCC) is situated at West Drayton, Middlesex and is responsible for the Area Control function in the areas shown on the diagram, up to 55°N. As considerable traffic is generated at Manchester a sub-centre has been established there to provide an area service both to that airfield and Liverpool and certain parts of the airways around where the aircraft are flying below 13,000 ft.

The Scottish Air Traffic Control Centre (ScATCC) is situated at Prestwick and its area of responsibility begins at 55°N and goes up to 61°N and is bounded to the east by the Norwegian and Danish FIRs. To the west it is bounded by the Oceanic Control Area. Between them the various ATCCs provide an air traffic service that encompasses all of the airspace contained within the UK FIR boundaries. The volume of this airspace is considerable and in order to be made more manageable the LATCC area is divided into sectors. These are

**Right** *General sectorisation of airspace controlled by LATCC.* (Produced from information supplied by the CAA.)

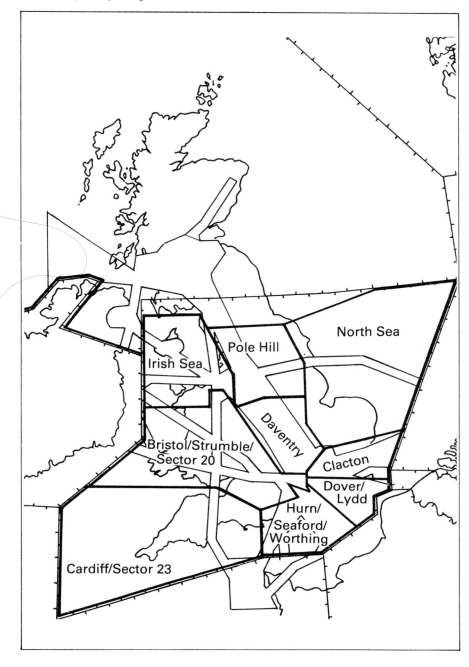

North Sea

Pole Hill

Irish Sea

Daventry

Bristol/Strumble/ Sector 20

Clacton

Dover/ Lydd

Hurn/ Seaford/ Worthing

Cardiff/Sector 23

designated as: Daventry, North Sea, Clacton, Dover/Lydd, Seaford/ Worthing/Hurn, Cardiff/Sector 23, Bristol/Strumble/Sector 20, and Pole Hill Irish Sea. The controllers working on each sector are responsible for all that happens within their sector under their jurisdiction and must carry out the necessary co-ordination with any approach, radar approach and aerodrome units that it encompasses. Additionally they must also co-ordinate the handover of an aircraft passing to the control of an adjacent sector and accept and comply with any restrictions imposed by the receiving sector. The same rule applies where the receiving sector is in the airspace of another country.

The operations room at the London Air Traffic Control Centre like those at Manchester and Prestwick operates for 24 hours per day, all year long. A shift system employing five 'watches' is in operation with approximately 400 Air Traffic Controllers and 200 Air Traffic Control Assistants being divided amongst the watches. Together with management, operations and technical support staff the total ATC workforce is in the order of 680 personnel.

The civil operations room at LATCC contains ten control suites sited on three sides and down the centre of the room. The super-

*The operations room of LATCC at West Drayton. (CAA.)*

visor's desk is sited on the fourth side. Each suite controls one of the areas already defined, the remainder catering for the London Terminal Area which is itself divided into TMA North and TMA South. Along the centre of the room are the en-route North Sea Sector, the Departure Flow Regulator Section and the Flight Plan Reception Centre. Also located in the operations room is the Flight Information Service, the FIR being split into three geographical areas, each manned by a controller. It provides an 'on request' Flight Information Service, an alerting service and proximity warnings to any aircraft known to be operating in the FIR outside of controlled airspace.

The en-route sectors are responsible for the airways and upper air routes in the areas they control as well as for any traffic crossing these routes. The TMA sectors are responsible for aircraft flying in airways below 13,000 ft within the TMAs and handle traffic destined for Heathrow, Gatwick, Northolt, Luton and Stansted airports. These aircraft are separated from each other and descended in a safe and orderly manner until they are approximately 25 miles from their destination where control is handed over to the destination airport's control.

*An en-route sector suite in the operations room of LATCC. (CAA.)*

On occasions when the quantity of traffic is too much for immediate routeing to destination, or delay is caused by bad weather, aircraft are routed towards one of the seven holding 'stacks' to hold in a racetrack pattern until they can be cleared onward. Upper levels of holding stacks are controlled by the TMA Arrival Controllers and the lower levels by the Approach Controllers at the destination airfield. Aircraft leave the stack in sequence to approach the landing runway. Aircraft departing the airfields are transferred to the TMA controllers soon after they leave the runway. The holding stacks in the London TMA are Biggin, Bovingdon, Lambourne and Ockham for Heathrow (with Epsom as a reserve when Ockham is out of use) and Willow, Eastwood and Mayfield for Gatwick, Mayfield being for traffic below 6,000 ft.

A control suite is staffed by a sector team the size of which will vary according to the airspace requirements and the level of traffic. The team leader is the Chief Sector Controller who will direct the work of all the personnel at the suite, and is responsible for the inter-sector co-ordination of all traffic entering or leaving the sector's airspace.

The Sector Radar Controller(s) control aircraft within the sector's airspace by maintaining radar surveillance and issuing executive instructions to pilots to ensure the safe and orderly flow of traffic. Control is provided to aircraft which are climbing or descending within the sector and to those over-flying and may involve the handling of as many as 12 aircraft at one time.

The Assistant Sector Controller is responsible for the provision and distribution of all air traffic data within and adjacent to the boundaries of the area controlled by the sector. He also carries out liaison with airfields, adjacent sectors and Air Traffic Control Centres.

The Military Controller is responsible for the co-ordination of military aircraft who wish to cross or join the civil air routes within the sector. Both military and civil controllers work closely together to ensure that military and civil aircraft can operate together in safety.

All sector teams enjoy the support of the Air Traffic Control Assistants who carry out general duties to relieve the control staff of the more routine tasks and telephone calls.

When a pilot intends to fly within the airspace controlled by LATCC, (or any other ATCC), he has to file a flight plan listing essential details about the flight, the aircraft, route, and destination.

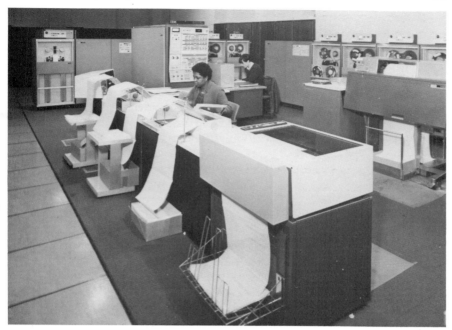

*The IBM 9020D computer equipment room at LATCC. (CAA.)*

The introduction of computer technology into ATC has enabled repetitive information to be stored and retrieved when required. An airline operating a regular daily flight from Heathrow to Glasgow or New York for example need only file one flight plan and that holds good until such time as there is a major change.

A Flight Data Processing System (FDPS) is built around an IBM 9020D computer so that, when flight plan data is fed into the system, the information will be passed automatically to all the controllers through whose area the aircraft will fly. Flight progress strips are printed giving the flight data and are placed on a flight progress board in geographical and time order. By comparing the required flight level and route with those already occupied by other aircraft the controller can plan a safe path for the aircraft. Any subsequent changes to say the flight level or route are fed into the 9020D computer and are relayed automatically to the appropriate sectors.

A 21 in diameter horizontal radar display is used by the Sector Radar Controller to monitor the progress of flights under his control. The area covered by the radar display also shows some adjacent sector airspace to give a better overall picture of the traffic situation. To ensure total coverage of sector airspace a selection of overlapping radars is available. Primary radar and secondary radar returns are processed before being presented on the display and each aircraft target is accompanied by a 'label'. This shows the aircraft's position, current flight level, and route or destination. Also shown on the display are the positions of en-route navigational aids, airways coastlines etc by means of an electronically generated video map.

It has already been stressed that no sector can work in isolation therefore it is necessary to provide a reliable and sophisticated communications system. ATC instructions are passed to pilots by VHF radio and each control position has a selection of up to 30 VHF radio channels. Direct access telephones are also provided to communicate with other LATCC controllers, other ATCCs and airfields. Access to an automatic telephone exchange is also provided. A 30-line telephone keyboard is available to the Chief Sector Controller whilst the other control positions have 20-line keyboards. Additional information is available by reference to four closed circuit television screens with a choice of ten channels. An electronic indicator also displays the up-to-date information on the visibility at the two main Heathrow landing runways.

Also situated at West Drayton are the London Military Radar Services who provide a radar service to aircraft operating outside controlled airspace. These services in order of priority are; aid to aircraft in distress, radar control of aircraft crossing the civil airways, centralised approach control service and a radar advisory service to aircraft in transit and flying below 24,500 ft. This service is only available if the aircraft are within radar cover and where the control capacity is available. A radar control or advisory service to aircraft on special tasks such as those flying on research and development is also provided.

Yet another service is provided by the military element at West Drayton in the operation of the Distress and Diversion Cell (D&D). When an aircraft transmits on the emergency frequency of 243 mHz (UHF) a number of forward relay stations pick up the transmission and present the aircraft's position pictorially on a screen in front of the D&D controllers. The D&D Cell has a large selection of direct land lines to a number of control agencies and has direct contact with the Rescue Co-ordination Centres at Edinburgh and Plymouth so that an aircraft in an emergency can receive the best possible help in the minimum of time.

The London Air Traffic Control Centre provides a comprehensive Air Traffic Control service to both civil and military aircraft and requires considerable support from the technical groups also employed there. This is provided from CAA and military sources and without it the unit as a whole could not function.

North of 55° N a very similar service is provided by the Scottish Air Traffic Control Centre (ScATCC) at Prestwick, for aircraft flying in the Scottish FIR. This FIR covers an area of approximately 137,000 square miles and is divided into sectors depending upon the density of the traffic. The Scottish airports of Edinburgh, Glasgow, and Prestwick are protected by the Scottish Terminal Control Area, comprised of three sectors to cope with the complex traffic patterns. The layout of the operations room at Prestwick is not dissimilar to that at LATCC and of course comprehensive technical support services are also provided. The operations room is again occupied by control suites, the west side of the room handling controlled and advisory traffic below 24,500 ft. The east side handles the civil upper airspace sectors whilst other suites on this side provide for control of

*The operations room at the Scottish Air Traffic Control Centre, Prestwick. The operational units are arranged in four rows with the outer rows consisting of control suites, each containing a planning and radar position. The units in the centre of the room provide back-up services including the flight data processing. (CAA.)*

*Air Traffic Control staff at work in the operations room of ScATCC. (CAA.)*

military traffic. The centre of the room is occupied by the various support services and desks are also provided for the civil and military supervisors. As well as having its own computer facility there is a direct connection to the IBM 9020D system at LATCC. ScATCC staff again work a five watch system, 24 hours per day, all year round and a watch consists of about 18 controllers and 18 assistants.

Prestwick also provides a service from the Oceanic Area Control Centre (OACC) for the North Atlantic Region. Responsibility for this control service is delegated by ICAO to five states; Iceland, Canada, USA, Portugal, and the United Kingdom, control being effected from the appropriate OACCs at Reykjavik, Gander, New York, Santa Maria, and Prestwick.

At first sight it would appear that the airspace over the North Atlantic would be sufficient to handle the needs of all those who wish to use it and it is difficult to envisage why it should ever become crowded. However, the differences in time zones, passenger demand, airport noise restrictions and the desire to use the best and most economical flight levels all combine to concentrate the traffic into a relatively narrow band of time, height, and breadth. This results in two main traffic flows, westbound in the morning and afternoon and eastbound in the late evening and early morning. In order to try and meet all the requirements a system of organised tracks is adopted and is constructed and reviewed by the relevant OACCs every 12 hours. The organisation of tracks is the responsibility of Prestwick OACC for the daytime system and Gander OACC for the night track system. The track planners on either side of the ocean consult with each other on a conference circuit and co-ordinate with adjacent OACCs and ATCCs as required. Having ensured sufficient track capacity to cope with the anticipated demand the organised track system is published by signal to all the interested units in Europe and North America. Any pilot then wishing to file a flight plan will know in advance the tracks available to him and can carry out his flight management planning well in advance. This system caters for the majority of flights crossing the North Atlantic from the UK and Europe and the USA but other flights do have to be accommodated. In these cases flight progress strips are prepared by hand rather than by computer but the basic intention remains the same, to ensure the safety of all the aircraft concerned.

The organised track system, although it applies on the North Atlantic routes, must be compatible with the domestic arrangement of airways and upper air routes. To this end organised tracks have specific entry and exit points at the boundary between oceanic airspace and the UK and Shannon FIRs. These entry and exit points are defined in whole degrees of latitude and longitude as under:
—49° to 51°N, all at 8°W, with the boundary to the west of Lands End and used by aircraft heading to and from that area.
—51° to 54°N, all at 15°W, with the boundary to the west of Ireland and used by aircraft heading to and from Cork, Shannon and 'Eagle' areas.
—55° to 61°N, all at 10°W, with the boundary to the west of Northern Ireland and used by traffic heading to and from the Belfast, Glasgow, Machrihanish, Benbecula, Stornoway and Sumburgh areas.

Also controlled by the OACCs are flights made by Concorde aircraft to and from the USA originating in both the United Kingdom and France. As the high flying supersonic aircraft is much less affected by wind and weather they operate along fixed tracks,

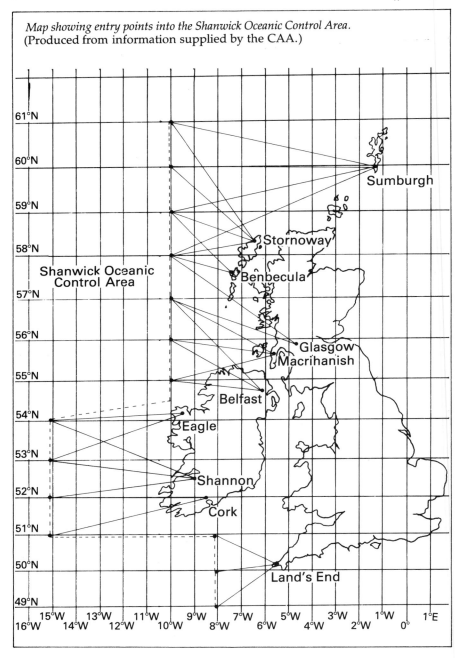

Map showing entry points into the Shanwick Oceanic Control Area.
(Produced from information supplied by the CAA.)

independant of the organised track system. Because of the limited number of flights involved it is very often possible for the OACC to issue an ocean clearance prior to take-off. This allows Concorde to adopt what is known as a 'cruise climb profile' which is best in terms of fuel economy. After the initial climb the aircraft is allowed to climb at its best speed and at a constant power setting. As fuel is burnt off and the aircraft becomes lighter it is allowed to climb further until it settles at around 50–60,000 ft. As with a car a light touch on the throttle and a constant demand on the fuel supply can pay handsome dividends in economy.

Much of the traffic which daily occupies UK airspace does not originate from there at all. A good percentage of the aircraft flying to and from the oceanic entry and exit points, for example, are generated by the nations on the continent of Europe and UK traffic also flies through the airspace belonging to other nations. For some time after World War 2 each nation looked after its own airspace with the boundaries defined as near as possible to their national boundaries. When much of the traffic was made up of slow piston-engined aircraft this presented no real problem. However when high performance jet airliners began to come into service in ever increasing numbers it became apparent that this type of aircraft could cover the ground so quickly that on some routes the changes from control centre to control centre were being conducted with unacceptable rapidity. To combat this problem and to bring a measure of standardisation to the Air Traffic Control service provided, six nations became signatories to the convention which set up Eurocontrol, the Organisation for the Safety of Air Navigation, which has its headquarters in Brussels. The original signatories at the setting up of the organisation in 1960 were Belgium, France, Germany, Holland, Luxembourg and the United Kingdom. Later, in 1965, Ireland was also to become a member.

Eurocontrol provides an air traffic service to all aircraft flying in the upper air space designed to ensure the safety of air navigation and to secure a safe and orderly flow of air traffic in the Eurocontrol area. As well as the provision of this service it forms an umbrella organisation to ensure a commonality of operational methods and procedures to be applied by its members. In many cases Eurocontrol carries out functions in research, training, and development very similar to that carried out by the CAA. The first international Upper Area Control Centre was set up in 1972 at Maastricht in Holland with a further centre being set up in 1975 at Shannon. A third centre, established in 1977, is at Karlsruhe in Germany.

With the acceptance of the need for a common approach to air traffic services came recognition that the cost of the provision of those services and their technical support could no longer be borne by individual members. In 1971 arrangements were put in hand for Eurocontrol to collect route charges for services provided within its area. In addition, agreement was also reached for Eurocontrol to collect route charges on their behalf for Austria, Portugal, Spain, and Switzerland.

The modern Air Traffic Control system consists of many parts, each one interdependant upon the others. This is true not only of national systems but of international systems too. In order to maintain the required level of understanding and co-operation, liaison visits are carried out by those who practise and plan the operational system. It must never be forgotten by those whose responsibility it is that the bright spot of light on a radar tube or the paper flight progress strip actually represents a real aircraft. Co-operation and understanding between controller and flight crew is vital and to further this aim controllers and certain members of the support staff have the opportunity to fly on a limited number of familiarisation flights every year. These flights are offered by many of the European airlines and some participating airlines from the USA. This enables control staff to observe their own system from the standpoint of the user and can only be beneficial to all concerned in the international business of Air Traffic Control.

# Chapter 9

# Radar in ATC

No other single invention has revolutionised the ATC system as has the adoption of radar and the modern ATC service could not have been developed without it. A composite word standing for radio detection and ranging, the principle was discovered and developed just prior to the beginning of World War 2 and during that conflict was further developed and refined into a number of distinct forms. Long and short range search radars were available as well as short range specialist radars in the form of Ground Controlled Approach Radar (GCA). Airborne radar was also available both for navigational purposes and for airborne interception.

Like many things which are technically complicated the basic operating principle is very simple. A radar aerial connected to a transmitter sends out a highly directional pulse of radio energy. If this energy strikes a target such as an aircraft some of that radio energy will be reflected and bounced back towards the aerial. Picked up and channelled into a receiver it can be displayed as a spot of light on a cathode ray tube. As radio waves travel at a known speed of 186,000 miles per second it is possible to measure the length of time taken for the pulse to leave the transmitter and return to the receiver and can be calculated as range. If the direction of the transmitted pulse is also known then it is a simple matter to calculate the target's position in range and bearing relative to the radar head. What does take some appreciating is the minute time scales involved. The time taken for a radar pulse to travel one nautical mile and return to its starting point is only 12.36 micro-seconds (a micro-second being one millionth of a second). A radar which operates upon this principle is known as a primary radar and

**Following page** *UK lower airspace radar advisory service.* (Produced from information supplied by the CAA.)

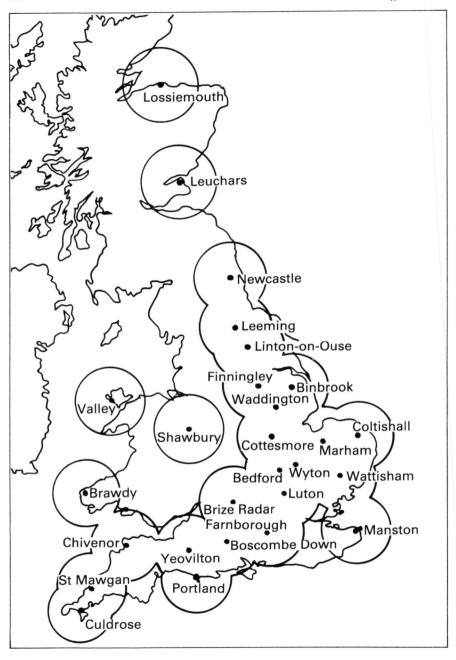

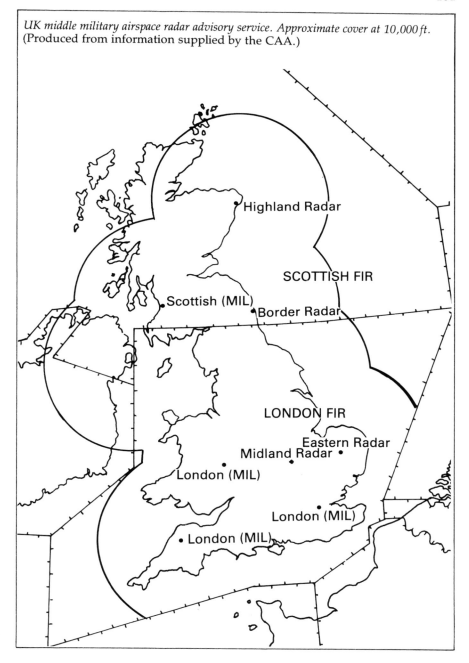

UK middle military airspace radar advisory service. Approximate cover at 10,000 ft. (Produced from information supplied by the CAA.)

*Plessey AR–1 Approach Radar installation.* (Photograph by the author, courtesy of the CAA.)

will produce a 'raw' radar picture. That is to say that it will pick up and display all objects that are capable of causing reflection of the outgoing pulse. As a result not only will it show aircraft but also high ground, high buildings, television transmitter masts and some types of heavy cloud. The radar returns from fixed objects are known as permanent echoes or PEs. In some radar installations it is necessary to have these PEs displayed such as in marine radar navigation where it is desired to see marker buoys and coastlines. However, generally in its application to ATC a display full of PEs only hinders rather than helps.

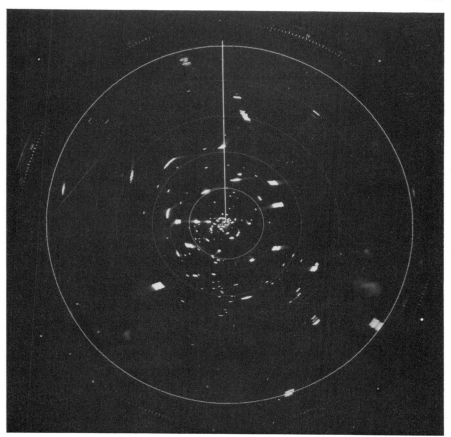

*A primary radar picture showing aircraft returns, permanent echoes in the centre and the north marker. (CAA.)*

To overcome this problem a device known as Moving Target Indicator (MTI) is used. This involves, in older equipment a time delay circuit, or in modern equipment a digital device, whereby the incoming pulse is held and compared with its predecessors. If the range has not changed then the returning echoes are suppressed and do not appear on the display. MTI can also be used to a limited range inside the total range of a radar. For example on a radar with a range of 50 nautical miles the MTI may be limited in its function to 25 nautical miles. Because radar transmissions are in the frequency range that travel on a line of sight, few ground based objects would be high enough to reflect the radar pulse from beyond the 25 mile range. It has the additional advantage of stopping any further attenuation at the longer range, the reflected portion of the outgoing pulse being only a fraction of its original strength. In ATC displayed primary radar is mainly used for Approach Radar Control, in DFTI and in ASMI.

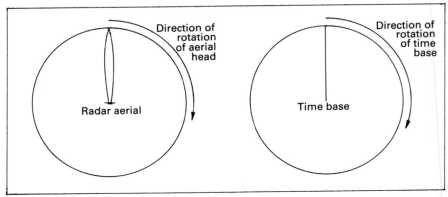

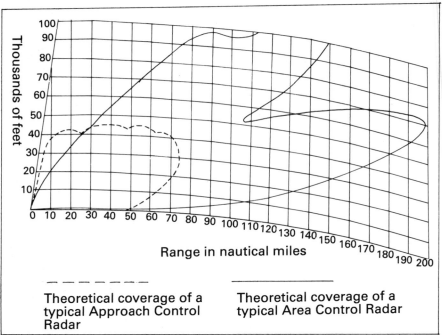

Theoretical coverage of a typical Approach Control Radar

Theoretical coverage of a typical Area Control Radar

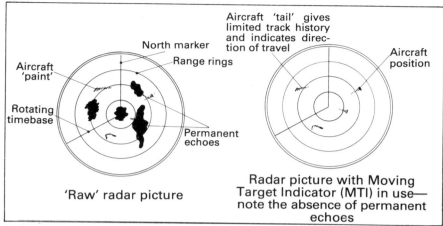

**'Raw' radar picture**

**Radar picture with Moving Target Indicator (MTI) in use— note the absence of permanent echoes**

**Left** *Diagram showing radar horizontal polar coverage. The radar aerial and the rotating time base revolve in synchronisation.*

**Below left** *Diagram showing radar vertical polar coverage.*

**Above** *Primary radar display plan position indicator.*

**Below** *A very sharp radar picture produced by the ASMI during trials at Edinburgh airport. The 'blip' at the end of the short disused runway is a Trident airliner now used for fire fighting training.*

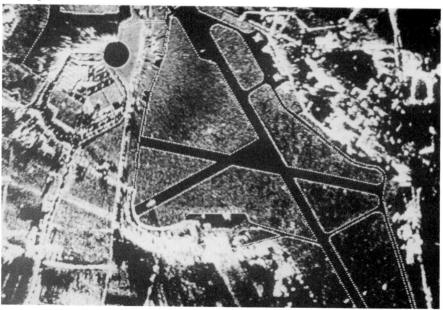

**Above** *A stand alone SSR installation.* (Photograph by the author, courtesy of the CAA.)
**Right** *Diagram explaining how SSR works.*

Another radar device developed during World War 2 has also been adopted in civil ATC. At a time when aircraft activity was at its peak it became necessary for defence radars to be able to identify friendly aircraft from enemy aircraft. This was done by installing in the friendly aircraft a device known as a transponder, in reality a transmitter/receiver which remained passive until interrogated by a search radar beam. When this happened the transponder was triggered to transmit a coded pulse to the ground station which in turn appeared alongside the primary radar return, positively identifying the aircraft as friendly. Known as Identification—Friend or Foe (IFF) this device was the direct forerunner of what is known today as Secondary Surveillance Radar (SSR).

Secondary radar also requires each aircraft to be fitted with a transponder. A simple selector switch on the aircraft's instrument panel allows the pilot to select the coded four figure response allocated to him by ATC as a discreet aircraft identity. This transmission is known as a 'squawk'. By introducing a computer into the decoding loop it is possible to carry out code to callsign conversion and this is displayed alongside the aircraft response together with information on the aircraft's height, route or destination. This 'label' moves across the face of the radar tube with the aircraft response and it is possible by using equipment on the radar console to reposition the label to avoid confusion when a number of aircraft are

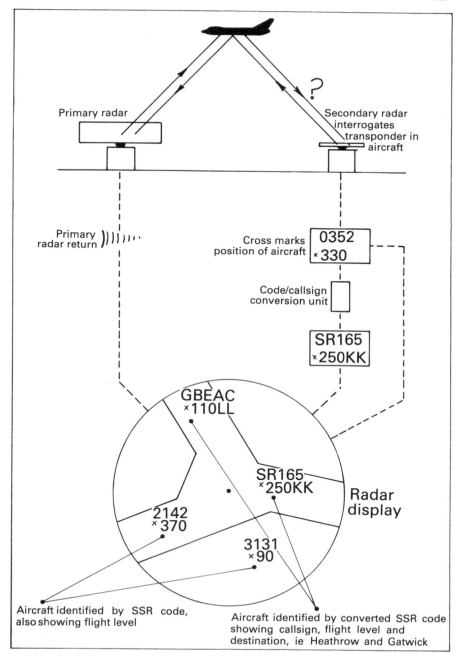

Primary radar

Secondary radar interrogates transponder in aircraft

Primary radar return )))))))

Cross marks position of aircraft

0352
× 330

Code/callsign conversion unit

SR165
× 250KK

GBEAC
× 110LL

SR165
× 250KK

Radar display

2142
× 370

3131
× 90

Aircraft identified by SSR code, also showing flight level

Aircraft identified by converted SSR code showing callsign, flight level and destination, ie Heathrow and Gatwick

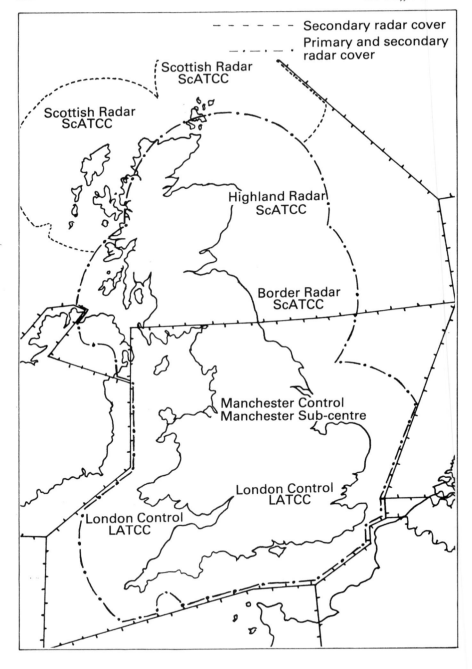

Secondary radar cover
Primary and secondary radar cover

Scottish Radar ScATCC

Scottish Radar ScATCC

Highland Radar ScATCC

Border Radar ScATCC

Manchester Control
Manchester Sub-centre

London Control LATCC

London Control LATCC

**Left** *Theoretical NATS primary and secondary radar coverage at 10,000 ft within UK FIR/UIR boundaries.* (Produced from information supplied by the CAA.)

**Right** *HSA 23 cm radar of the type now being installed as part of the CAA radar replacement programme. The large primary aerial is below with a 'hog trough' secondary radar aerial mounted above.* (Photograph by the author, courtesy of the CAA.)

so close together that their labels become superimposed. Because SSR uses a transmitted pulse it has an advantage in that the power of the transmitter can be reduced considerably. The ability to receive coded information, particularly that relating to height is extremely useful as it is not easily achieved by other radar means. Height finding radars are mainly used for military purposes and are then confined to judging comparative heights between a target and an interceptor. Such a radar has no civil application as at ranges from 50–60 miles a vertical separation distance of 1,000 ft is hardly discernable.

Both primary and secondary radars are used by ATC. On some sites they are co-located but with separate aerial heads whilst on others the SSR aerial is mounted on top of the primary radar head.

This reduces the problems associated with trying to synchronise two independantly rotating radar heads.

The principle method of controlling traffic at LATCC is by using radar. Both primary and secondary radar information is fed into the centre from remote radar stations so positioned to give the best possible coverage to the area of operation. These remote radars are sited at Heathrow Airport, Ash near Canterbury, Ventnor on the Isle of Wight, Clee Hill, Shropshire, Burrington, Devon and at St Annes in Lancashire. An additional secondary radar service is available from Mount Gabriel in Ireland and is provided on an agency basis by Eurocontrol. This installation extends SSR coverage out to 15°W.

It is a basic principle throughout aviation, including ATC, that where a vital function is reliant upon a particular device that there shall be adequate back up facilities available if the primary device should fail in service. So it is with the area radar system, each radar site being carefully chosen so that there is adequate overlap between the coverage provided by one radar site and another. At LATCC the incoming radar signals are fed into the IBM 9020D Flight Data Processing System (FDPS) for processing before the information is displayed. This method known as the Processed Radar Display System (PRDS), brings together the primary and secondary radar information together with that provided by the SSR code to callsign conversion data and presents to the controller a target mark with its associated data label. Added to this is a computer generated map so that the controller has presented to him a complete visual picture of the area under his jurisdiction.

The 9020D PRDS can provide a mosaic radar picture and does this by dividing the London FIR into 16 nautical mile squares. Each of these squares employs radar cover from a 'preferred' radar and a 'supplementary' radar and although the 'preferred' radar data is normally used the 'supplementary' radar data can be substituted automatically in the event of failure. All of the radar data displayed is, of course, presented in such a fashion that it can be readily associated with the appropriate flight progress strips.

An Approach Radar unit operates in a much smaller geographical area and provides the following services; surveillance radar approaches, radar vectoring and sequencing for an ILS or radar approach, radar monitoring of an ILS approach, radar control of departing aircraft and radar control of aircraft in transit through the Approach Control area. The Approach Radar unit will only assume control responsibility when the aircraft has been released to it from Area Control or when the aircraft enters the area of responsibility from outside controlled airspace.

In practice the work of the Approach Radar is very much influenced by such conditions as the weather, the amount of traffic, and the serviceability of ground aids. In light traffic and good visibility it is perfectly possible that the pilot of an approaching aircraft will advise Approach Control that he can see the airfield and wishes to carry out a visual approach. In this case the approach function will act as a monitor only.

In medium traffic loadings the Approach Radar unit will sequence aircraft as they are released to them passing control instructions on height, heading, and speed the aim being to arrange the aircraft on the ILS so that there is a minimum of delay. A separation distance of not less than three miles is normally used unless there are other factors to be considered for example turbulent wake. This works well at airfields like Heathrow with parallel runways where the inbound and outbound aircraft use separate runways. However at busy airfields such as Gatwick or Manchester with only single runway operation co-ordination may have to be effected between Approach and Air Controllers in order to get outbound aircraft away. In either case the aim is to turn the aircraft onto the ILS centre line guidance beam at around seven to eight miles at a height of 1,500 ft. This allows the pilot to settle the aircraft down and prepare to capture the ILS glideslope before commencing final descent.

In heavy traffic where direct routeing is not possible aircraft are directed to a holding stack, marked by a radio beacon. The first aircraft into the stack goes in at the lowest available level, subsequent aircraft entering at levels 1,000 ft apart where they hold in a racetrack pattern until released for approach. The majority of racetrack patterns are known as one minute patterns. This means that the aircraft flies up to the beacon and makes a rate one turn (180° in one minute) then proceeds on the outbound leg for one minute before making a second rate one turn back towards the beacon. Thus the time taken to fly a complete pattern is four minutes. The major axis of the holding pattern is laid down for every designated stack as is the direction of turn. This and the location of holding stacks is carefully worked out to avoid any conflict with other departing or transiting traffic. On those mercifully few occasions when delays are really bad it may become necessary to hold traffic en-route and before it reaches an already full stack. In this event any

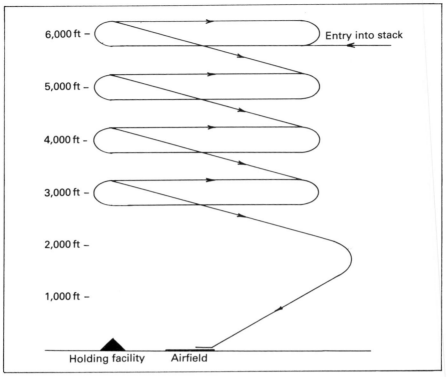

*The holding stack.*

convenient en-route radio beacon can be used but in this case the
major holding axis will have to be defined but is usually co-incident
with the direction of the airway.

London (Heathrow) has four stacks situated at Bovingdon to the
North of the TMA, at Lambourne to the North-east of the TMA, at
Biggin Hill to the South-east of the TMA and at Ockham to the
South-west of the TMA. Similarly there are stacks at Willow and
Eastwood to the South and South-east of Gatwick. Aircraft departing a Heathrow stack do so under the control of a Radar Director
there being one Director per stack. Between them they have to
sequence their aircraft into a single stream, not an easy task with
aircraft originating from four different sources. The stack system
enables ATC to control large numbers of aircraft and to organise an
orderly approach sequence with the minimum of delay. As aircraft
leave the stack at a low level the remaining aircraft are also de-

scended in the stack until they too are released for a radar guided approach. The only occasion when an aircraft may jump the queue in a holding stack is if an emergency is declared.

The Approach Radar Director may also conduct Surveillance Radar Approaches (SRA) where the type of radar and the radar site is approved for this purpose and where the radar display shows the final approach track and ranges from touchdown. The range from touchdown at which an SRA must be terminated is laid down and may be a prescribed point not more than two miles but not less than half a mile from touchdown. The aircraft is descended and sequenced in the normal way to a point where it intercepts the extended runway centreline and a nominal glide path. Pre-computed advisory heights, allied to the range from touchdown, are passed to the pilot at every half mile to enable him to maintain the nominal glide path. The half mile checks apply when the range at which the SRA must be terminated is also half a mile. In this case too the Radar Director is not expected to undertake any duties other than those directly concerned with that particular SRA.

When the termination range is two miles the Radar Director will pass advisory heights at every mile of range. If, at the termination of the SRA, or at the company imposed decision height, or at the laid down obstacle clearance limit, it is not possible for the aircraft to be landed visually then it will carry out a missed approach. At this point the pilot may elect to go around for another try or he may decide to go to his diversion airfield.

The Distance From Touchdown Indicator (DFTI) has already been briefly described in a previous chapter and the Airfield Surface Movement Indicator (ASMI) was also mentioned. The latest ASMI, now undergoing acceptance trials at Gatwick, has a number of features not previously available. The well defined picture made possible by the short operational range and the aerial turning rate of around 60 rpm makes this a useful aid anyway. As an extra on the Gatwick installation it is possible to use the display with more versatility. It has a (comparatively) long range scale available which allows the Air Controller to look at the approach in the event of a failure of the DFTI. Conversely, at the other end of the scale, it is possible by positioning a cross on the tube face by means of a 'joystick' to enlarge a selected portion of the airfield for closer examination. The radar information is displayed in three positions in the VCR giving access to the Air Controller, the Ground Movements Controller, and the Airfield Lighting Assistant.

Although the description of the uses of radar and the services it enables ATC to offer is necessarily brief it will be appreciated that without it the ATC system would be incapable of handling the quantity of traffic that it does. At the present time a major radar re-equipment programme is under way to replace many of the now ageing radars currently in service. These are shown in the accompanying diagram together with an indication of their effective range in plan view. The effective coverage of any radar is governed initially by its designed power output and its siting and surrounding terrain. For these reasons the actual performance of any given radar will vary on different sites. In order to ascertain the actual performance each radar is calibrated by observation against known factors and by using specially equipped aircraft. This work results in the radar calibration experts being able to plot accurately the beam width known as the horizontal coverage diagram and the coverage in the vertical plain known as the vertical coverage diagram. Accurate knowledge of the coverage of a radar is absolutely vital as more and more of the computer based ATC systems depend on information which is radar derived.

# Chapter 10

# Services provided for and by ATC

Just as a railway does not consist solely of track, locomotives and rolling stock, so the air traffic service units previously described do not form the only parts of the total ATC system. There are other services which are provided either directly by the CAA or are provided by other agencies. Taken together they complete the picture as a whole. The following are services provided by the CAA.

## The Joint Airmiss Section (JAS)

As the title implies, this section has no dividing line of responsibility between the activities of civil and military aircraft. The very word 'airmiss' can of itself conjure up horrific mental pictures of near catastrophy as two aircraft hurtle past each other with only inches to spare. Although it would be dishonest to pretend that this never happens, it is thankfully rare and the majority of airmisses are not as fraught as this. Airmiss reports are filed by one or both of the pilots involved if they consider that their aircraft may have been endangered by the proximity of another during flight within UK airspace and it is believed that a definite risk of collision existed. The report may be filed by R/T if loading permits this, otherwise it should be filed as soon as possible after landing. The information required includes the position and time of the incident, the altitude or flight level and whether the aircraft was climbing, descending, or in level flight, the aircraft heading and the weather conditions at the time and place of the incident. A brief description of the incident is also required to include the first sighting of the conflicting traffic and the estimated miss distance.

Whatever the cause and whoever is involved all airmiss reports go to the Officer Commanding the JAS for co-ordinated investigation into the cause. It may be that the error originated in a piece of equipment, in the system, or was caused by human error. However the basic aim is to find out how it happened and to avoid any repetition. By putting all airmiss reports through a common investigatory procedure it is possible to discern any 'trend' in the pattern of airmisses and to recommend alterations to particular areas of operation.

## The Airspace Utilisation Section (AUS)

The users of UK airspace are many and varied. In order to achieve the most safe, efficient and economical use the Airspace Utilisation Section was set up in 1975 to cater for those who wished to participate in what is described as 'unusual aerial activity'. This term covers such activities as flying displays, parachuting, crop spraying, aerial surveys, military exercises and many other activities which, for one reason or another, are unable to comply with the standard rules. It is the responsibility of the AUS to co-ordinate the requests for the special use of airspace and to notify other users of the activity and the time and place of the event. This achieves the flexible use of airspace and contributes in no small way to overall safety by ensuring that all users are correctly informed.

## The Aeronautical Information Service (AIS)

The international nature of air travel creates difficulties peculiar to that form of travel. It is all very well to decide to fly to say Copenhagen or Rome on the blind assumption that all will be in order on arrival, but what if it is not? Searching around for somewhere else to go is not only wasteful it is positively dangerous. Safe and efficient air travel be it for sport, business, or commercial purposes depends upon the availability of good information which in its turn allows pilots to properly plan their flights. To facilitate this planning the Aeronautical Information Service (AIS) is charged with collecting, collating, editing and disseminating aeronautical information necessary for the safety and efficiency of air navigation to all interested parties including operating companies, aircrews and other aviation organisations. It is also able to receive post-flight information.

Each flight information region has its own AIS centre located for convenience at a major airport within its region. These centres provide a 24-hour service and their function is to originate NOTAM Class 1 Information received from the aerodromes and other outstations within their region. This is despatched via the aeronautical fixed service to the International NOTAM Office at Pinner in

Middlesex, to other AIS centres and to all other interested aerodromes within the United kingdom.

A NOTAM is a foreshortened title derived from 'Notice to airmen'. They are divided into NOTAMS Class 1, which are distributed by teleprinter, and NOTAMs Class 2 which are distributed by postal means. NOTAMs Class 2 are further sub-divided into Series A, information other than temporary navigation warnings, and Series B, temporary navigation warnings. Put simply Class 1 is used for the transmission of urgent information such as the sudden and unexpected closure of an airfield for operational reasons and Class 2 for the transmission of non-urgent information such as the planned night closure of an airfield to allow the carrying out of resurfacing work at a pre-planned date.

AIS aerodrome units are located at certain major airports and are manned by briefing officers. These units maintain a full information service. At other aerodromes a self briefing unit may be established, carrying a limited amount of information and abridged information on foreign aerodromes and services. At international airports within the United Kingdom the AIS unit will prepare, at intervals, information bulletins to cover the destinations which its flights regularly serve. This method allows a pilot to pick up the latest information in a form which is readily useable in his pre-flight planning.

Member States of ICAO are required to provide an Aeronautical Information Service as set down in Standards and Recommended Practices in May 1953. Member States are also required to publish an Aeronautical Information Publication or AIP. The AIP should contain all the information necessary for any aircraft, national or foreign, to make a flight into or through that country. It is divided into sections, each identified by an abbreviated title. The AIP published for the United Kingdom is known as the United Kingdom Air Pilot. Originally published as a single volume it is now enlarged to three volumes and is the 'bible' of ATC and aviation.

The volumes and sections are as follows:

**Volume 1**
**RAC** (Rules of the Air and Air Traffic Control): ATC regulations and procedures, air traffic systems, holding and departure procedures, altimeter setting procedures and restricted airspace.

**Volume 2**
**GEN** (General information): AIS, general regulations and miscel-

laneous information, differences in standards, abbreviations used, time system, dimensional units and registration marks.

**AGA** (Aerodromes and ground aids): International airports and airports available for use by international traffic, an aerodrome directory, and aerodrome lighting.

**COM** (Communications): Radio and navigational aids, location indicators, navigational systems and time signals.

**MET** (Meteorology): Details of meteorological stations, offices and broadcasts.

**FAL** (Facilitation): Airport regulations for entry, exit, transit and charges.

**SAR** (Search and rescue): Facilities available.

**MAP** (Maps and Charts): The provision of the above.

**Volume 3**
**CHART** Actual maps and charts used in aerial navigation

The United Kingdom Air Pilot is a very comprehensive document and contains a wealth of information but it will be appreciated that a document of this nature is only of real value if it is constantly updated. The Aeronautical Information Service is the medium by which this is done.

Flight Clearance is a generic term used to denote a position where a pilot can contact ATC and can file a flight plan. Its location on an airfield is usually denoted by a black letter 'C' on a yellow board. At many airfields the flight plan is received by ATC staff who meet the pilots directly, discuss any details and process the flight plan form ready for entry into the system. A flight plan can mean either the full information as required on the flight plan form or limited information required to obtain an ATC clearance for a portion of a flight such as crossing an airway or flying in a control zone. However, the destination airfield is only advised of the flight details if it covers the entire flight. Flight plans may be filed on the ground at least 30 minutes prior to the estimated time of departure. Alternatively an airborne flight plan can be filed via the R/T provided that ATC is given sufficient time to arrange a clearance before penetration of controlled airspace. An ATC clearance is normally issued 10 minutes before such penetration.

A flight plan is the pilot's 'entry ticket' into the ATC system and *may* be filed for any flight. However, a flight plan *must* be filed by a pilot if he intends to conduct his flight as follows:

—For all flights within controlled airspace notified as being Rule 21.

That is airspace deemed to be permanently subject to the Instrument Flight Rules.

—For all flights within controlled airspace which are conducted in accordance with the Instrument Flight Rules.

—For all flights where he wishes to participate in the ATC advisory service.

—For flights within certain Special Rules Areas/Zones, irrespective of any weather conditions.

—For flights which cross a UK international FIR boundary.

—For any flight where the destination is greater than 40 km from the aerodrome of departure and the aircraft maximum total weight exceeds 5,700 kg.

A pilot is advised to file a flight plan if he intends to fly over the sea more than 10 miles from the coastline of the United Kingdom or over sparsely populated areas where search and rescue could be difficult. A pilot is also advised to file a flight plan if he intends to fly into an area where search and rescue operations are in progress. The flight plan must include an estimate of the time of arrival and departure from the search area. Details of any such flight will be notified to the relevant Rescue Co-ordination Centre.

## Services provided to the CAA

The weather plays an important and sometimes unpredictable part in the operation of the ATC service particularly at aerodromes. ATC is supplied with meteorological information from the meteorological office. A controller is expected to brief himself on the weather and forecast weather for the areas related to his duties. He may do this by studying the information supplied by the meteorological office or by a personal briefing. If neither are available to him he can obtain a briefing by telephone. As a general rule a controller may only transmit to an aircraft information that has been supplied, or agreed, by the meteorological office. There are, however, exceptions.

A controller may transmit the wind speed and direction where there are anemometer indicators fitted in the control room. He may also transmit information on Runway Visual Range (RVR), about which more later. The safety of aircraft being of paramount importance, a controller may decide to pass information on a sudden or unexpected deterioration of the weather which he has observed. Another source of information which may have to be passed on quickly is observations made by pilots in flight. A report from an aircraft on the presence of unexpectedly severe weather would be passed onto other aircraft transitting the same general area together with the information that the report originated from an aircraft and the time at which the observation was made. In any event if the aircraft observation indicates the presence of severe icing or turbulence it will always be communicated to other aircraft and passed as soon as possible to the meteorological office who will decide whether the condition warrants the issue of a special report. A controller may also pass information on cloud echoes observed on radar.

At aerodromes where there is no meteorological office, ATC staff who have been certified by the meteorological office as having satisfactorily completed an approved course of training may make and pass on weather observations. Controllers are always expected to keep a close watch on the weather, reporting as required and may be asked to obtain weather information from aircraft.

The meteorological office issue routine weather reports for an aerodrome either hourly or half hourly as required and those reports contain the following information:
—The time of the observation.
—The surface wind speed and direction.
—The general visibility in increments of 100 m when it is 5,000 m or less and in whole kilometres when it is greater than 5,000 m.
—The general weather, ie fog, rain, snow, etc.
—Cloud—layers of cloud with amounts expressed in oktas (eighths) and the height of the cloud base in feet above aerodrome elevation. The presence of cumulonimbus clouds, which very often give rise to thunderstorms, icing, and severe turbulence, are always reported when they are in the vicinity of the aerodrome.
—QNH—The barometric pressure at sea level.
—QFE—The barometric pressure at aerodrome level.
—The surface temperature and dew point in degrees Celsius.
—A remarks section for use if needed.

Additionally the meteorological office may issue a special report when there is a specific improvement or deterioration of any of the items contained in the routine report. In a routine report the term CAVOK (Ceiling and visibility—OK), transmitted as CAV-OK may be used when all of the following conditions are met at the same time. The visibility is 10 km or more, there is no precipitation, thunderstorm, shallow fog or drifting snow and there is no cloud below 5,000 ft above aerodrome level and no cumulonimbus cloud at any level. Put another way, a fine summer's day.

SIGMET (Significant meteorological information) messages are issued when particularly severe meteorological conditions are expected to endanger flight safety. These conditions include the presence of active thunderstorms, tropical revolving storms, line squalls, heavy hail, severe turbulence, severe airframe icing, marked mountain waves (updraught), or widespread dust and sandstorms. Put another way, anything but a fine summer's day! SIGMET messages are amended if necessary due to changing conditions and are cancelled as soon as the specific condition ceases.

The measurement of visibility as supplied by the meteorological office has, by its very nature, to be a general assessment. However in conditions of fog and low visibility it is essential for the pilot to have available a more localised and accurate assessment made in relation to the runway in use. This localised assessment is known as Runway Visual Range (RVR) and is measured when the meteorological office assessment is 1,500 m or less. The RVR value, expressed in metres indicates to the pilot the range over which he can expect to see the runway surface markings or lights delineating the runway edge or centreline. RVR measurements may be made by one of two methods, either by human observation or by using special electronic measuring devices. In the latter case, and to differentiate between the two methods the measurement is known as Instrumented Runway Visual Range (IRVR).

Assessment of RVR by the human observation method involves the setting up of a Runway Observation Post (ROP). The ROP is sited to one side of the runway and adjacent to the touchdown zone and is of sufficient height to allow the observer to view the runway from an elevation approximating to that of the pilot. The observer counts the number of runway edge lights he can see and refers this to a conversion table which indicates the distance in metres. This value is then passed directly to the control tower for transmission to aircraft. Obviously it is important that these observations are as accurate as possible and to this end the runway edge lighting at airports is checked by special teams, initially to establish the lights to be used for the measurement of RVR and thereafter at intervals to ensure that the calibration remains valid. These teams operate from the Air Traffic Control Evaluation Unit at Bournemouth. Observation commences when the visibility as assessed by the meteorological office is reported as 1,500 m or less and continues until the reported visibility is in excess of this figure and the RVR is in excess of the maximum measurable distance. In practice, because of the layout of runway lighting and the limitations of the human eye the maximum RVR distance that can be practically assessed is usually around 1,100 m. Once RVR has been established every significant change, ie a change of one or more increments, has to be reported. The human observation method requires a great deal of skill and balanced judgment to be exercised by the observer. It is quite likely that the slipstream of a departing aircraft will bring about a dramatic but short lived improvement in RVR. It is, however, hardly worth reporting this as the RVR will quickly return to its previous value.

For a number of years the author was involved in duties that included the observation of RVR. It is most eeerie to be out on a fog shrouded airport at night, knowing that a very large and very solid aircraft is approaching and will, given a lot of skill and some luck, flash past you onto the runway. It may only be visible for a few seconds. Thoughts on personal vulnerability are not cheered by the realisation that you are housed in a structure which is officially described as 'frangible'. In other words if the aircraft is off the centre line towards your side the structure in which you sit will offer no protection whatsoever, disappearing in a shower of firewood. The fact that all structures near a runway, including ILS aerials, are built on the same principle of minimum resistance to an aircraft's passage is no comfort either. A new ILS can always be got from stores!

The human observer method described above worked well for many years until the length of runways reached a point where the RVR observation covered only a relatively small percentage of the total length. On a runway with a length of say 3,050 m to 4,575 m there can be a considerable difference in the visibility along its length. This can be potentially very dangerous particularly if the aircraft lands or begins its take-off roll in a relatively clear patch only to run into thick fog half way along. To overcome this problem the second system, Instrumented Runway Visual Range (IRVR) was introduced. This method gives an accurate assessment of RVR at three different locations along the length of the runway. These positions are at the touch-down zones at each end of the runway and as near as is practicable to the mid-point along its length. For the purposes of R/T transmissions the three locations are referred to as 'Touchdown', 'Mid-point', and 'Stop End'.

Devices known as Transmisometers are used to measure atmospheric opacity and the data obtained from the three observation positions is fed by an associated data transfer system into a central

*An IRVR 'Dalek', normally sited in facing pairs at three locations alongside the runway. (Photograph by the author, courtesy of the CAA.)*

processor. The processor combines this data with other information such as the intensity of the runway lighting and computes the RVR. The RVR is then continuously displayed in all of the ATC operations rooms concerned. The operational range of the equipment extends from zero to 1,500 m in a number of incremental steps as follows:

—50–150m in steps of 25m.

—150–800m in steps of 50m.

—800–1,500m in steps of 100m.

The criteria for IRVR reporting is that the official general meteorological report shows the visibility to be 1,500 m or less, the IRVR value is observed to be 1,500 m or less, or shallow fog is reported or is forecast.

Yet another weather information service is available to pilots. This is known as VOLMET and is a routine broadcast of meteorological information to aircraft in flight. A continuous loop tape system is used to record half hourly weather reports from airfields giving observations made at 20 minutes past and 10 minutes to every hour. The elements of each report are broadcast on a continuous basis in the following order:

Surface wind, visibility, RVR (if applicable), weather, cloud, temperature, dewpoint and QNH. Non-essential words such as 'surface wind, visibility', etc are not broadcast. A pilot can obtain the information he requires by tuning into a published frequency. If, for example, he is tuned into the London Volmet (Main) he will be able to receive weather reports for London (Heathrow), London (Gatwick), Birmingham, Manchester International, Prestwick, Dublin, Amsterdam, Brussels, and Paris/Charles-de-Gaulle. A similar service is also available identified as London Volmet (South), and London Volmet (North). These give information appropriate to their area.

**Chapter 11**

# *ATC and the airfield*

With suitably equipped airfields and aircraft offering the ability to operate successfuly in even the lowest of visibilities it is apparent that the siting and type of airfield lighting has also to be of an acceptable standard. A landing successfully executed in thick fog can quickly be reduced to farce if the pilot cannot then find his way off the runway, follow the taxyways and thence to the apron. Because of the varying requirements of different airfields and even for different runways within the same airfield it is not possible to describe a 'typical' airfield lighting system. However, by inter-

*Critical positions in the aerodrome traffic circuit. The drawing illustrates a typical left-hand circuit. In position 1 the aircraft reports on downwind leg when abeam the upwind end of the runway. In position 2 the aircraft reports on base leg. In position 3 the aircraft reports on 'finals' and receives clearance to land. An aircraft in position 4 reports on 'long finals' when it is between four to eight miles away. Clearance to land may be issued at this time or the aircraft may be told to continue and call again at four miles distant, this will depend upon the traffic situation at the time. (Produced from information supplied by the CAA.)*

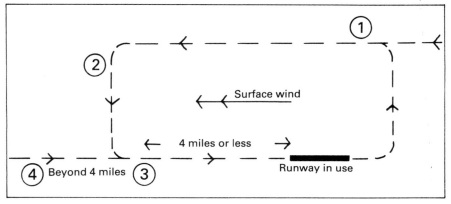

Surface wind

4 miles or less

Beyond 4 miles

Runway in use

national agreement through ICAO there is standardisation regarding the colour of airfield lighting and what the colours indicate.

*Runway side lights*—White
*Runway centreline lights*—White, but red towards the Stop End
*Taxyway edge lights*—Blue
*Taxyway centreline lights*—Green
*Stop bars*—Red
*Threshold (Touchdown)*—Green
*Threshold (Stop End)*—Red
*Approach lights*—White
*Crossbar lights*—White
*Obstruction lights*—Red

The standard and layout of approach and runway lighting then is directly allied to the category of the landing aids available. The lower the allowable minima for approach and landing the better the lighting must be. No matter what the standard the basic idea behind airfield lighting remains the same, to give a pilot visual guidance and to enable him to recognise ground features and locate his position with some accuracy.

In a very simple system the runway edges and ends will be marked by lights showing the limit of their extent. An extended centreline will also have at least one crossbar of lights to provide a

**Left** *Form and proportion of numbers and letters for runway designation markings. Runway designation markings indicate the magnetic heading of the runway when viewed from the approach so a runway marked 24 would be on a heading of 240°. At airfields with two parallel runways each designator is supplemented by a letter eg 28L (left) and 28R (right). Where there are three parallel runways the letter C is used to indicate the centre runway.*
**Below** *Typical runway markings.*

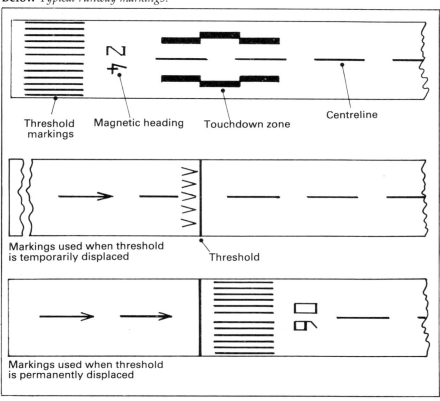

Threshold markings  Magnetic heading  Touchdown zone  Centreline

Markings used when threshold is temporarily displaced  Threshold

Markings used when threshold is permanently displaced

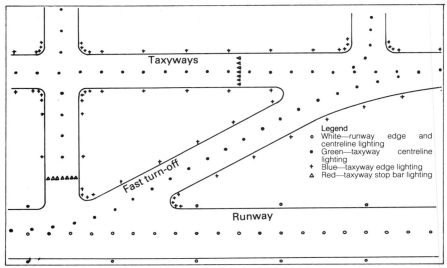

*Typical aerodrome lighting.*

'horizon'. What this system does not give, especially to the pilot who sees the lights very late in an approach after breaking out of low cloud say, is any accurate indication of where he is along the extended centreline and therefore how far he is from touchdown. To overcome this deficiency a development of the basic system was introduced which 'coded' the lighting information. A single line of lights on the extended centreline goes out as far as the first crossbar. The centreline lights then become two parallel rows of lights out to the second crossbar. At this point the centre line lights become three parallel rows of lights out to the final crossbar. Now the pilot can tell at a glance which third of the approach lighting he is looking at and can judge more accurately his distance from touchdown.

The above system, but with considerable lighting additions, is in use at international airports on the main instrument landing runways. Runway edge, threshold and centreline guidance is still provided but the touchdown zone and the runway centreline are also illuminated. In amongst the fixed approach lights are strobe lights which flash in sequence along the approach path up to the threshold beckoning the pilot onwards to the runway and safety. Once on the runway surface the pilot is required to find his way to the apron along a routeing given to him by ATC. Again in a simple system the taxyways are marked by blue edge lights whilst on international airports and other airfields the taxyway is marked by green centreline lighting. The change in aircraft design partly dictated the need to change from edge markings to centreline markings on both taxyways and runways. In a straight winged aircraft with good visibility from the cockpit it is relatively easy to judge where the aircraft actually is in relation to the centre of the tarmac. On a 'Jumbo' with its cockpit set high and well forward of the bulk of the aircraft little is visible to judge distances and the wing tips may not be visible at all. It becomes much simpler to drive straight down a line of green lights. As an additional aid to the pilot, on a runway with an illuminated centreline, the white lighting becomes interspersed with red lights towards the Stop End, with the final stretch marked wholly in red lights up to the red threshold bar at the runway's end. This indication gives the pilot a quick visual check on the runway remaining if he lands long or has to abandon a take-off. For safety reasons also obstructions such as ILS aerials, buildings, hangars etc, are marked with red obstruction lights.

From the public viewing gallery or a road adjacent to an airport the pattern of lights can be wholly distorted and therefore meaningless. From the flight deck of an approaching aircraft the pattern assumes its intended order and provides essential visual reference to enable a night or bad weather landing to be accomplished successfully.

Another area of airport operation which is vital to the safety of aircraft is the assessment of the braking action on the duty runway. This assessment is made when there is known to be standing water,

*Airfield approach lighting.*

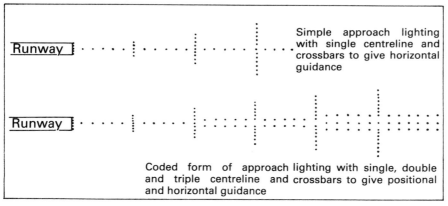

*A high-powered lighting installation for apron illuminations. Being close to the flying area it also carries a red obstruction light.*

ice, snow or slush on the runway, any one of which can markedly affect the ability of an aircraft to stop or remain under directional control. In these circumstances the responsibility for the measurement of assessment of the runway conditions rests with the airport authority although special arrangements are made at some airfields for this responsibility to be delegated to the air traffic service unit.

Measurements are made approximately 10 m on either side of the runway centreline which corresponds with the average wheel track width. As a first step it is necessary to identify what the problem is and definitions do exist as to what should be categorised as dry snow, wet snow, slush, etc. Two methods are employed in measuring the co-efficient of friction, the first using a brake testing decelerometer known as a Tapley Meter. This is placed on a level plain on the floor of a vehicle which is then driven at a steady 25 to 30 mph. At areas where it is desired to check the braking action the vehicle brakes are firmly applied until all four wheels lock. The Tapley Meter will then indicate a peak value for the co-efficient of friction. Measurements are made at approximately 300 m intervals along the runway length and to either side of the runway centreline. The Tapley Meter method will give a good indication of the braking conditions but must not be used to measure the braking action in slush or when there are thin deposits of wet snow when significant inaccuracies can occur. As well as providing an indication to the pilot of the runway surface conditions he is likely to encounter on landing or take-off, driving such a brake test vehicle is no mean test of the vehicle handling ability of the driver! More than one braking check has witnessed an unscheduled excursion into parts of the airfield hitherto unvisited.

A more up to date method involves the use of a Mu-Meter which is in fact a runway friction measuring trailer towed behind a vehicle at a constant 40 mph. This is always used for measuring braking action on a wet runway when a significant amount of water is standing on the surface and is likely to affect braking action and directional control. During the test runs a continuous register of the mean co-efficient of friction provided by means of a paper trace recorder or a digital read-out that is used in conjunction with a hand computer. Later equipments incorporate a remote read-out device which simplifies the conversion of the figures obtained into their frictional values. The mean value for each third of the runway length can then be determined. Braking action is assessed as either Good, Medium/Good, Medium, Medium/Poor or Poor.

Measurement of the depth of snow or slush is also necessary and is taken using a standard depth gauge from 5 to 10 m either side of the runway centreline. A mean reading is arrived at for each third of the total runway lengthy. The need for a constant check on runway surface conditions during periods of bad or very cold weather will be appreciated. However it is also necessary to carry out routine checks of the airfield generally.

The responsibility for carrying out aerodrome inspections is with the aerodrome authority but may, by special arrangement, be delegated to the air traffic service unit. Aerodrome surface inspections should be made at least once per day and at aerodromes which are open round the clock this should be as soon as is practicable after

*Airport fire tender. The monitor above the cab is for laying down large quantities of foam to smother an aircraft fire rapidly.*

first light. At aerodromes not providing a 24-hour service the inspection should take place before flying commences. Inspections are carried out from a vehicle driven slowly over the paved surface of the airfield, particular attention being paid to the main runway and its associated taxyways. The observer should check for any damage to the surface including loose stones, and that runways, taxyways, stopways, and holding areas are free from obstructions and that any temporary obstructions on or adjacent to the runways or taxyways are properly marked or lit. A similar inspection is carried out after dark to check upon the serviceability of the aerodrome lighting. The observer should also keep a good look out for concentrated groups of birds. An aircraft suffering a bird strike can be severely damaged especially if the bird or birds are ingested by an engine. It doesn't do the birds a lot of good either! Various methods have been tried over the years to remove concentrations of birds from airfields. These range from the controlled use of birds of prey, the firing of special bird scaring cartridges, to the broadcasting of bird distress calls via loud speakers mounted on specially equipped vehicles. All of these methods can be successful but this success is generally short lived, almost as if the birds are reminding man that they had a claim on the airspace long before he came along with his rules and regulations and his noisy aeroplanes.

Another group very much concerned with the safety of aviation on the airfield, and directly linked to the air traffic service unit is the Aerodrome Emergency Service. Comprised of a number of fire and rescue appliances this service is available continuously during the hours of operation of the aerodrome. The numbers and types of fire/rescue appliances which go to make up the emergency service is governed by the type and frequency of the traffic the aerodrome usually handles. In the event of their being called out to an accident or incident the emergency fire and rescue cover will be re-provided by the outside brigades. It is the fervent wish of all, of course, that they are never needed 'in anger' and thankfully this is generally the case.

Before leaving the confines of the airfield one other aid to pilots has to be described. A pilot making a visual final approach and descent to the runway uses a number of visual clues to accurately position and hold his aircraft on the correct line and in the correct attitude to complete a succesful landing. He refers to the actual horizon or, at night, approach light crossbars, to maintain his wings in a level position. Directional guidance comes from being able to see the tarmac stretching ahead or from the approach centreline and runway lighting. What he has not got, yet, is any external visual indication of the required glide slope to enable him to descend at a constant rate to arrive on the touch-down zone of the runway.

This guidance is provided by one of two systems both of which

*Pilot's view of Visual Approach Slope Indicators.*

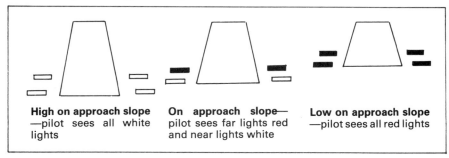

**High on approach slope** —pilot sees all white lights     **On approach slope—** pilot sees far lights red and near lights white     **Low on approach slope** —pilot sees all red lights

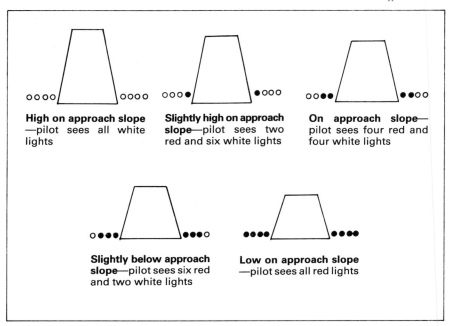

**Above** *Pilot's view of Precision Approach Path Indicators.*

**Below** *Typical layout of landing aids (radio and visual) and IRVR measuring equipment.*

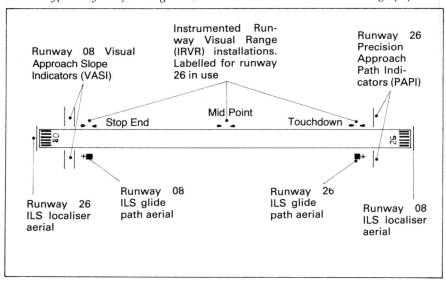

operate on the same basic principle, that is of projecting a well defined beam of light back along the approach path. Although the light source is white the fitting of coloured filters has the effect of coding the information as seen by the pilot. The two systems are Visual Approach Slope Indicators (VASI) and a more recent and more accurate development, Precision Approach Path Indicators (PAPI). Both systems require a number of light boxes to be positioned at the sides of the runway adjacent to the touch-down zone. The pilot making an approach to a runway equipped with VASIs will see two bars of light on either side of the runway. If he is properly on the glide slope the bar of light furthest away will be red and the nearer one white. If he is too high both bars will be white and if too low both will be red. These lights are visible over a range of several miles and enable an aircraft to make a long steady approach either by day or night.

The newer system of PAPI was originally developed to assist the pilots of short take-off and landing (STOL) aircraft to carry out a precision touch-down on a runway of restricted length, following a stable approach with adequate safety margins. The PAPI installation consists of two lots of four lights, one set on either side of the runway. If the approach is too high the pilot will see eight white lights, if slightly high, one red light next to the runway edge and three white lights either side. When he is positioned correctly he will see four red lights and four white lights, and if too low, eight red lights. The PAPIs give an extremely accurate visual indication of the correct glide slope angle and are aligned so that the touch-down point they indicate is co-incident with that indicated by the Instrument Landing System. As pilots are now able to operate in conditions of really low visibility the higher accuracy of aids the better and better yet if more than one system points the safe way home. PAPIs are also fitted at a number of military airfields.

**Chapter 12**

# A flight using the system

Air Traffic Control is about rules and regulations, aircraft and airways, equipment and communications. It is also about people. People who have been fortunate enough to become involved in a job which requires dedication, skill, professionalism, and simple caring. Since the days of the early aviators, historically portrayed as swashbuckling characters in leather jackets and flying helmets, there has been a tendency for those of the aviation fraternity to make light of the job they do and the responsibility it entails. It has spawned a protective language all of its own, for example calling a crash a prang, and there are many others now absorbed into everyday usage. However, whatever front any individual may choose to hide behind, they all know the rewards to be had for getting it right and the terrible penalty to be exacted for getting it wrong.

In the preceding chapters the various pieces of the 'jigsaw' of ATC and aviation have been examined and it is time to put all of the pieces together and view the overall picture. We will begin by joining the crew of an aircraft on an internal flight from Bournemouth to Edinburgh.

It is 06:30 on Saturday morning, late in the month of October on a grey, wet and windy day when we arrive at Bournemouth's Hurn airport. We make our way from the car park to the welcoming lights and warmth of the terminal building, there to meet our captain. Our aircraft is a Hawker Siddley 748 twin turbo-prop airliner, an aircraft built in some quantity and in use all over the world. The crew today is comprised of two pilots, two stewardesses, an as yet unknown number of passengers and yourself along for the ride and to see how it all works. After being introduced to our captain he would normally set out who is to do what on the ground before departure, however, for the purpose of letting you see the whole operation the

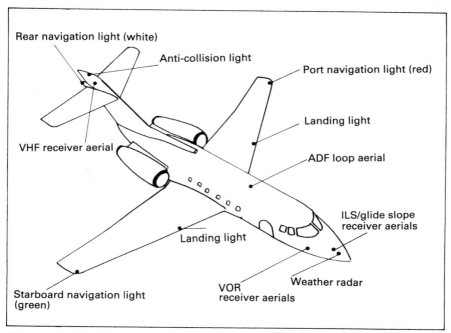

*Diagram showing the typical distribution of lights, receiver aerials and weather radar. The aircraft is a British Aerospace 125.*

flight deck crew will stay together. With a departure time of 08:00 there is much to do so the sooner started the better.

Before going out to the aircraft it is necessary to complete the formalities on this side of the airfield. Our first port of call is at the meteorological office where we can check the weather at our point of departure, en route, and at our destination. We also have to check the weather at any airfields nominated for use in the event of diversion. In this case the choice is simple, our alternative to Edinburgh will be Glasgow. As our flight is going to carry us the length of England and on into Scotland the first thing to check is the overall weather picture. This is presented to us on a pictorial chart similar to that shown on television but without the moveable illustrative symbols used by the weathermen. Of all the many different influences that can effect the conduct of a flight only one remains constant and that is the ever present weather. Many years of costly experience has shown that failure to take proper account of the present and forecast weather can be a big mistake, on occasion

one for which the maximum penalty is paid. In other words our visit to the met office is no mere formality.

The weather chart shows a high pressure region well to the south and centred over Spain. To the west and south of Ireland is a low pressure system of 983 millibars and just to the north and west of Scotland is another low pressure system of 992 millibars. As the wind always travels around a high pressure system in a clockwise direction in the northern hemisphere and a low pressure system in an anti-clockwise direction, the combined effect of the present pressure system is to produce a wind from the south west over the whole of our route. This wind is also moist, having crossed many miles of ocean, but it will give us a tail wind component and help us on our way. A warm front has recently passed through the area and is now out over the North Sea whilst an associated cold front straddles the centre of England. The isobars, lines which join points of equal barometric pressure, are spaced fairly well apart which indicates light to moderate winds all the way up through the altitude bands.

We can now look at the current and forecast weather for our airfield of departure. The actual weather is observed, a report prepared and disseminated every 30 minutes, timed at 20 minutes past and ten minutes to every hour. The area forecast weather for Bournemouth is as follows:

—Surface wind: 210° at 10–15 knots.
—2,000 ft wind: 230° at 30 knots becoming 35 knots.
—5,000 ft wind: 230° at 35 knots becoming 40 knots.
—10,000 ft wind: 230° at 35 knots becoming 45 knots.

The wind is always quoted in degrees and indicates the direction from which the wind is blowing. The surface visibility is 4,000 m to 6 km but 2,000 m in drizzle. Airframe icing is forecast as light but locally moderate and there is a warning of hill fog with visibility as low as 200 m. Cloud consists of a broken overcast with a base of 200 to 500 ft and a top of 1,000 ft. Above that broken strato-cumulus with a base of 1,200 ft and a top of 8,000 ft is going to mean a climb out on instruments. Higher still broken cloud with a base of 12,000 ft in thin layers up to a layer of cirrus-stratus at 25,000 ft.

The Edinburgh weather is: surface wind—200° at 19 knots but gusting to 32 knots; surface visibility is 15 km in rain; cloud amounts

*The type of aircraft in which the flight is to be made, an HS748. (CAA.)*

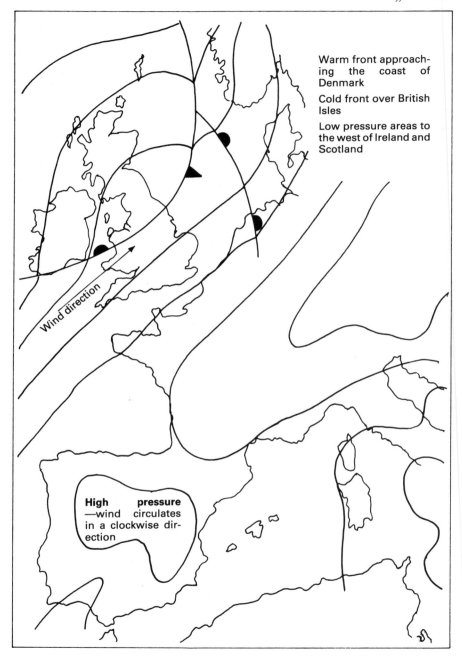

Warm front approaching the coast of Denmark

Cold front over British Isles

Low pressure areas to the west of Ireland and Scotland

Wind direction

**High      pressure** —wind circulates in a clockwise direction

are 1 octa at 1,200 ft, 3 octa at 9,000 ft, 8 octa at 12,000 ft; outside air temperature is +15°C.

The Glasgow weather is very similar, a typical wet and windy autumn day. The weather pattern is not going to influence any change in our choice of route so, other things being equal, we will be routeing via Amber 25 and White 9. What might still influence the choice of route would be any major unserviceability in the en-route or landing navigational aids.

To check these we next visit the office of the Aeronautical Information Service (AIS). The information here is constantly updated so that what we learn is correct at the time it is checked. Additionally, advanced information will be available on any aids due to be taken out of service for routine maintenance or flight checking. Once again we discover nothing to influence our choice of route so the next step is to file the flight plan, our entry ticket into the ATC system.

A flight plan is written out onto a standard form, not all of which is completed by the crew, and is designed to give the ATC system the maximum amount of information as to the pilot's intention whilst presenting it in an easily readable and standardised format. Block capitals should be used throughout and all clock times are inserted in four figure groups, GMT.

The first item required on the form is the aircraft identification which may be the international registration markings of the aircraft itself or a recognised radio telephony callsign for the aircraft operating agency. In our case the operating identity is ADAIR 56. The next piece of information required is the type of flight rules to be operated under (IFR or VFR) and the type of flight, ie scheduled or non-scheduled air transport, general aviation etc. The weather being what it is and the fact that from Brecon onwards we shall be in controlled airspace it will be an IFR flight all the way (I), being made by a scheduled transport (S). Our next entry then is IS.

On the next line the numbers, if more than one, and the type of aircraft is required together with our wake turbulence category which is medium. This is entered as HS74/M. Then follows a coded entry to show what communication, navigation and approach aid equipment is carried on the aircraft and is serviceable. As ours is standard for the route being flown the entry is S.

**Left** *The weather at the time of the flight.* (Produced from information supplied by the Meteorological Office.)

CAA C(G)6 Drg No 7838A 3·5·78

| FLIGHT PLAN | ATS COPY |
|---|---|

| PRIORITY INDICATOR **FF** | ADDRESSEE (S) INDICATOR (S) | 《≡ |

| FILING TIME | ORIGINATOR INDICATOR | 《≡ |

SPECIFIC IDENTIFICATION OF ADDRESSEE (S) AND/OR ORIGINATOR

| 3 DESCRIPTION | 7 AIRCRAFT IDENTIFICATION | 8 FLIGHT RULES AND TYPE OF FLIGHT | |
|---|---|---|---|
| 《≡( FPL — | ADAIR 56 — | I S | 《≡ |

| 9 NUMBER & TYPE OF AIRCRAFT & WAKE TURBULENCE CATEGORY | 10 COM/NAV/APP EQUIPMENT SSR | |
|---|---|---|
| — HS 74 / M | — S/C | 《≡ |

| 13 AERODROME OF DEPARTURE & TIME | FIR BOUNDARIES & ESTIMATED TIMES |
|---|---|
| — EGHH 0800 | → |

《≡

| 15 CRUISING SPEED     LEVEL | ROUTE |
|---|---|
| — 0240 F120 | → DCT BCN A25 DCS/W9 |

《≡

| 17 AERODROME OF DESTINATION & TIME | ALTERNATE AERODROME(S) | |
|---|---|---|
| — EGPH 0930 | → EGPF | 《≡ |

| 18 OTHER INFORMATION |
|---|
| — RMK/RED ARR |

)《≡

| 19 SUPPLEMENTARY INFORMATION — NOT FOR TRANSMISSION | | |
|---|---|---|
| ENDURANCE | PERSONS ON BOARD | EMERGENCY & SURVIVAL EQUIPMENT |
| — FUEL / 0330 | → POB / 29 | → RDO / 121·5 → ~~243~~ |

| EQUIPMENT | | LIFE JACKETS | | FREQUENCY |
|---|---|---|---|---|
| ~~POLAR~~ → ~~DESERT~~ → MARITIME → ~~JUNGLE~~ → | | JACKETS → LIGHT → | FLUORESCEIN → | |

| DINGHIES | COLOUR | NUMBER | TOTAL CAPACITY | OTHER EQUIPMENT |
|---|---|---|---|---|
| DINGHIES → COVER | YELLOW | 04 | 048 | → RMK / |

| | NAME OF PILOT – IN – COMMAND | SIGNATURE OF PILOT – IN – COMMAND OR DESIGNATED REPRESENTATIVE |
|---|---|---|
| )《≡ | A. A. JONES | *signature* |

CA48/RAF F2919 (Revised August 1978)

The aerodrome of departure is entered next, together with our estimated time of departure. As previously explained airfields are allocated ICAO four letter indicators and that for Hurn is EGHH, so that here is written EGHH/08:00.

A much larger space now requires some entry. Ours is a straight forward flight but room has to be made for long flights or those with complicated routeings. Our entry here is under Cruising speed—Level—Route and is as follows: 0240F120 DCT BCN A25 DCS/W9. Decoded this means that we shall be cruising at 240 knots at flight level 120 going directly to the joining airway Amber 25 at the navigational beacon at Brecon, thence via similar navigational aids at Knighton and Wallasey to Dean Cross. At this point we travel along airway White 9, still at the same speed and flight level to Talla and then to Edinburgh. The ICAO code for Edinburgh is EGPH and our estimated time of arrival 09:30 so that on the next line down we enter EGPH 09:30, together with the declared alternate airfield which is Glasgow or EGPF.

'Other information' now follows so that we can add anything which is relevant to make a simple request of the ATC system such as requesting the ATC Unit at our destination airfield to notify by teleprinter signal our airfield of departure of our safe arrival. Thus we enter RMK/REQ ARR.

This completes the basic flight plan, although other information must be entered at this time it is not for onward tansmission. This information is only relevent in the highly unlikely event that we meet with misfortune en-route when it will be needed quickly if we are to receive maximum assistance from any rescue effort. In the spaces provided we enter our total fuel load expressed in hours and minutes of flying time, the total number of people on board, the radio frequency of our emergency and survival equipment, the fact that we carry life jackets with lights and flourescein dye, and that we also carry four dinghies with yellow covers and a carrying capacity of 48 people. Finally, the flight plan form is signed by the captain being the pilot in command. The completed form is handed into the Flight Clearance Office of ATC where it is scrutinised as far as possible for accuracy and for acceptability within the ATC system. At this point we will leave it for a while and continue with the flying side of the journey.

**Left** *The flight plan as completed by the pilot and submitted to ATC as a statement of intent. Wherever possible requested routes and flight levels will be granted.*

CAA C(G)6 Drg No 7838A 3·5·78

| FLIGHT PLAN | | ATS COPY |
|---|---|---|

| PRIORITY INDICATOR **FF** | ADDRESSEE (S) INDICATOR (S) | *EGTTZØFP* *EGCCZØ* *EGPXZØ* *EGPHZA* | ≪≡ |
|---|---|---|---|

| FILING TIME *0700* | ORIGINATOR INDICATOR | *EGHHZP* | ≪≡ |
|---|---|---|---|

SPECIFIC IDENTIFICATION OF ADDRESSEE (S) AND/OR ORIGINATOR

| 3 DESCRIPTION | 7 AIRCRAFT IDENTIFICATION | 8 FLIGHT RULES AND TYPE OF FLIGHT | |
|---|---|---|---|
| ≪≡( FPL — | *ADAIR 56* — | *IS* | ≪≡ |

| 9 NUMBER & TYPE OF AIRCRAFT & WAKE TURBULENCE CATEGORY | 10 COM/NAV/APP EQUIPMENT SSR | |
|---|---|---|
| — *HS74* / *M* | — *S/C* | ≪≡ |

| 13 AERODROME OF DEPARTURE & TIME | FIR BOUNDARIES & ESTIMATED TIMES | |
|---|---|---|
| — *EGHH 0800* | ← | |
| | | ≪≡ |

| 15 CRUISING SPEED | LEVEL | ROUTE | |
|---|---|---|---|
| — *0240* | *F120* | ← *DcT BCN A25 DCS/W9* | |
| | | | ≪≡ |

| 17 AERODROME OF DESTINATION & TIME | ALTERNATE AERODROME(S) | |
|---|---|---|
| — *EGPH 0930* | ← *EGPF* | ≪≡ |

| 18 OTHER INFORMATION | |
|---|---|
| — *RMIK/REØ ARR* | |
| | )≪≡ |

| 19 SUPPLEMENTARY INFORMATION — NOT FOR TRANSMISSION | | |
|---|---|---|
| ENDURANCE | PERSONS ON BOARD | EMERGENCY & SURVIVAL EQUIPMENT |
| — FUEL / *0330* | ← POB / *29* | ← RDO / 121·5 ← ~~243~~ |

| EQUIPMENT | LIFE JACKETS | FREQUENCY |
|---|---|---|
| ~~POLAR~~ ← ~~DESERT~~ ← MARITIME ← ~~JUNGLE~~ ← | JACKETS ← LIGHT ← | FLUORESCEIN ← |

| DINGHIES | COLOUR | NUMBER | TOTAL CAPACITY | OTHER EQUIPMENT |
|---|---|---|---|---|
| DINGHIES ← COVER | *YELLOW* | *04* | *048* | ← RMK / |

| | NAME OF PILOT – IN – COMMAND | SIGNATURE OF PILOT – IN – COMMAND OR DESIGNATED REPRESENTATIVE |
|---|---|---|
| )≪≡ | *AA JONES* | *AA Jones* |

CA48/RAF F2919 (Revised August 1978)

**Above** *The crew of an RAF Dominie complete their walk round inspection of the aircraft.*
**Left** *The flight plan as completed by ATC prior to transmission on the AFTN to the ATCCs and other ATSUs concerned. Information is extracted from this form to prepare flight progress strips.*

It is time to pick up our flight bags containing all the necessary charts and manuals and venture forth into the rain towards the aircraft, at about the same time the public address system in the passenger lounge is calling forward our prospective passengers. In many ways this walk across the airfield apron to the aircraft can be the most potentially dangerous part of the whole trip. This is especially true at busy international airports where a lot of aircraft might be on the move or about to move and all amid a great deal of noise. It is all to easy to pass dangerously close to a running jet engine. To get around this problem it is standard practice to select 'on' the red rotating anti-collision lights just before the first engine is started.

Our aircraft has now been on the ground for some hours but before being parked for the night will have undergone an engineering check and been fueled. The latter is done to reduce any chance of condensation in the fuel tanks allowing the fuel to become water contaminated. The first thing to be done is to undertake a physical walk round of the aircraft. This external examination is done

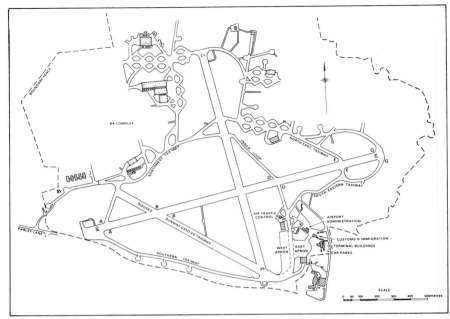

*Bournemouth (Hurn) airport.* (Reproduced by permission of the CAA.)

systematically, beginning at the nose and working steadily round until we arrive back at the nose again. That which can be checked visually or by touch will be checked. Particular attention is paid to looking for any signs of structural damage, fuel, oil, or hydraulic leaks, the condition of tyres and the security of inspection hatches. Satisfied that all is as it should be and that nobody has driven a vehicle into the aircraft during the hours of darkness our attention is turned to the technical log as presented by the ground engineer. Here are listed the serviceability states of the various component functions of the aircraft, together with any technical snags still being carried. Provided that any listed snag is considered not to affect the safety of the flight and is acceptable to the pilot in command minor snags will be accepted. The pilot also checks the life of certain items on the aircraft as shown in the log against indicated life. For example, the engine of the family car tends to run until it becomes very evident that all is not well. At this point remedial action may or may not be taken dependant upon it being convenient, affordable or whatever. On an aircraft, employed on passenger transport duties in particular, no such leeway is allowed. All components are 'lifed' depending upon design and operational experience and when that life is exhausted they must be replaced or renewed. Satisfied that all is well the captain will sign the technical log to indicate his acceptance of the aircraft and its technical condition.

As we settle into our seats prior to bringing the aircraft to life our passengers will have completed the formalities and will shortly be brought out to the aircraft, settled into their seats and have all hand luggage safely stowed. While this is going on the aircraft is drawing its power supply from an external ground power unit. This can be a tractor towed unit or self propelled and supplies the aircraft with electrical power and, in some cases, compressed air. Now the work in the cockpit begins, check lists are gone through and various items of equipment switched on and tested. The company representative appears to present the load sheet showing the number of passengers, the weight of baggage, the total operational weight of the aircraft etc. The load sheet too is signed to indicate acceptance of the details shown. Just about now the senior stewardess will appear on the flight deck to report that all are aboard and the cabin, her domain, is ready. She will also call the attention of the crew to anything unusual about the passenger load such as the presence of invalids, babies, pregnant women or anyone else she thinks might need a special mention or attention.

While this has been going on the first officer has been busy with the cockpit work, including checking the radios with the tower, and the aircraft can now start up. This is preceded by a 'start up' call to the tower to indicate that the flight will be ready shortly for an ATC clearance. With the anti-collision lights flashing to indicate to others the imminence of our start the attention of the pilot is now centred on the ground engineer. He will carry out a final visual safety check and then holding one finger aloft he will make a circular motion with his other hand—clear to start number one. Engines are numbered from the port or left hand side of the aircraft so that on a multi-engined aircraft the one furthest out on the wing is always number one.

The crew will monitor the start on their cockpit engine instruments whilst the ground engineer watches for any signs of abnormality or fire. When the port engine is running satisfactorily the ground engineer will transfer his attention to the number two engine, carry out his visual safety check and extending two fingers in the air indicates that the crew can start number two. Once that is done, and upon a sign from the cockpit that the aircraft is now on internal power, the ground engineer will move into the aircraft to disconnect the ground power unit cable. By this time the first officer will have checked the radios with the tower and selected various aids and services. The wheel chocks are waved away and the ground power unit will depart, the aircraft is now ready to move. Taxy clearance is requested and this will be given as far as the runway holding point together with the instructions on routeing.

Power is gently increased and the aircraft rolls forward under the control of the captain. As the aircraft moves away a short period of intense activity begins. The flying control surfaces are checked for full and free movement, and a check of all instruments is made to see that those which should be indicating something actually are. As the direction of travel changes as taxyways are joined or crossed the navigational guidance instruments from the magnetic compass to the VOR indicator will also be watched to ensure that they record the change of direction. ATC will also come up with the departure clearance which must be written down and read back where, as in our case, no standard instrument departure is used. It also has to be checked to see that it is realistic in concept for that aircraft on that particular flight. It may well be that other aircraft are taxying ahead of us and they too must be looked out for.

In the middle of all this a number of pre-determined check lists are also being run through. Finally, just before entering the runway comes the pre take-off list including a check that the 'No Smoking' and 'Fasten Seatbelt' signs are illuminated and that the cabin staff have reported that their end of the aircraft is set to go.

At some stage during this period the captain will also brief his first officer on emergency actions to be taken during say an abandoned take-off, a fire or some other unforseen hazard. The captain does not always do the flying but he always bears the ultimate responsibility so that if he has delegated and something goes wrong there must be absolutely no doubt if and when he has retaken control. To this end the statement 'I have control' is short, sharp, and unambiguous. To the observer these often cryptic exchanges can sound odd or mildly amusing but they are there for a reason. In an emergency, especially in an aircraft with a large flight deck crew it is vital that everyone understands the situation and what is expected of them. There is a story of a large piston-engined airliner that had safely completed a landing when the captain asked the flight engineer to 'take off power'. Roused from his reverie the unfortunate engineer promptly poured on 'take-off power' which isn't quite the same thing and by the time it was all sorted out the aircraft was through the hedge at the end of the runway.

Over the radio comes clearance to line up and take off together with a surface wind check. On comes the power, off come the brakes and away we go. As the speed builds up the first officer will call out a number of speed checks that have been calculated previously. The first of these is 'V1', the go or no go decision speed. If anything goes seriously wrong before 'V1' is reached then sufficient runway remains for the aircraft to be brought to a stop in safety. The next check is 'VR', the speed at which the aircraft can be rotated and will lift off. The last of these checks is 'V2', which is the safe climb out speed if an engine is lost at or after 'V1'. On hearing 'VR' called the pilot eases back on the control column, the rumbling of the undercarriage ceases and we are airborne. A gentle squeeze of the brakes stops the wheels rotating, the undercarriage is retracted and the flaps are selected up. The aircraft is trimmed to climb steadily at around 1,000 ft per minute and the turn to the right made to take us towards the navigational beacon at Brecon. When settled the crew will switch the 'No Smoking' and 'Fasten Seat Belt' signs off.

Being a well run, if fictitious, airline we were airborne at exactly 08:00 and estimate Brecon at 08:26. We call clear of the control zone boundary and call London FIR to announce our presence and request an airways joining clearance at Brecon. Our request is acknowledged and we climb steadily upwards in the rain and cloud towards our first beacon. At this time we are not under positive control being in the FIR, however we will be advised of the presence of any known conflicting traffic and we can also make use of the radar advisory service. As we are flying in the FIR we must obey the Quadrantal Rule and being on a north westerly heading we must stop our climb at an even flight level plus 500 ft. On this occasion the captain elects to climb as far as FL 105, approximately 10,500 ft, which will keep us clear of most of the cloud. Some 14 minutes after take-off we announce our arrival at this level to the London FIR controller and repeat our estimate for Brecon.

We will also be treated to a cup of coffee by the cabin staff. Even this simple action has a safety aspect. Coffee is announced rather than suddenly presented otherwise an unexpected arm movement might empty the contents all over the instruments or electrics which is not considered to be a good idea. The captain will also make the first announcement over the cabin address system. This will be

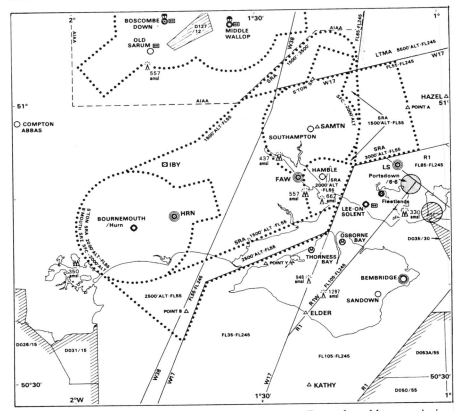

*The Southampton and Bournemouth special rules airspace.* (Reproduced by permission of the CAA.)

welcoming and informative. It serves a dual purpose—not only does it inform the passengers of the progress of the flight together with any information of interest, it also serves to reassure any nervous or first time passenger that there really is someone on the other side of the cockpit door who is wide awake and has everything under control.

The aircraft is cruising steadily on when we receive our airways joining clearance. We are cleared 'to join Amber 25 at Brecon at FL 120 to be level at FL 120 by Brecon'. We are also given our SSR squawk or identity code and instructed to call London Radar on the appropriate radio frequency, the Bristol/Strumble sector. The SSR code is selected and we will now show as an identifiable radar return. We also leave FL 105 climbing to reach FL 120 by the time we enter controlled airspace. At 08:26 we arrive overhead the beacon and turn gently to the right heading for the VOR at Wallesey. Our aircraft is now fully in controlled airspace and we enjoy the full protection this affords. Our estimated time of arrival over Wallasey is 08:51 which is passed to the radar controller over the R/T.

All of this however did not just happen by good fortune. When we handed in our flight plan it set the system in motion long before we ourselves left the ground. On receipt by ATC of the flight plan at Hurn the following actions were carried out. An aerodrome outbound strip was prepared and the flight plan itself was then addressed to the Flight Plan Processing Section at the London Air Traffic Control Centre, to the Manchester Sub-centre, to the Scottish Air Traffic Control Centre and to the Approach Control Unit at Edinburgh and transmitted to them on the AFTN. The LATCC 9020D system will produce the flight progress strips needed to record our flight and will also cause similar flight progress strips to be produced at the Manchester Sub-centre. At our planned flight level of 120 we will transit through the airspace controlled by them so they need advanced warning of our coming, our intentions and our eventual destination. Similarly ScATCC and Edinburgh will prepare the flight progress strips they need to record our passage. All of these strips are prepared with estimated times over reporting points, based on our flight plan information, and these are updated as required once we become airborne. The flight progress strips are used to record the history of our flight and all other flights under the control of the same sector. This enables the controller to assess the traffic patterns in his area and any areas of conflict. In effect we have 'booked' FL 120 to Wallasey and beyond so that it will not be offered to another aircraft whose flight path is in conflict with ours. By being able to project forward in time it is possible to control and manage the traffic in an orderly and efficient manner.

Back in the aircraft as it flies towards Wallasey we are able to listen into and occasionally see other aircraft who share the same airspace. Coming towards us now but 1,000 ft lower is a BAC 1-11 out of Manchester, bound for Mallorca. He is only visible for a few seconds before flashing by. The figure of 1,000 ft sounds quite large but it always appears closer than it really is and it is not difficult to appreciate the chaos that would ensue were it not for the existence of the ATC system.

Just south of Rexham (spelled without the silent W on airways charts for the benefit of foreigners) we are handed over to the control of the Manchester Sub-centre who have already received a telephone handover from LATCC. We bid London 'Good day' and announce our presence on the Manchester frequency, giving call-sign, flight level, and our estimate for Wallasey. All of this is already known to the Manchester controller but it serves to confirm that we still have two-way contact with the ground and that the information he has before him is correct. The VOR at Wallasey serves to mark a busy aerial junction. Passing through are Amber 25 running north/south, Red 3 running north west/south east and Blue 1 running east/west. It is also part of the inbound and outbound routeing for aircraft travelling to and from the many airfields in the north west. As we pass overhead we announce our presence to the controller together with our flight level and our forward estimate for Dean Cross VOR which we estimate at 09:11.

All this time the cockpit crew have been working away monitoring the progress of the flight and the technical state of the aircraft. A further cabin address has been made giving the local weather and our time of arrival in Edinburgh. Meanwhile we are now over the sea with the holiday resorts of Lancashire off to our right but not visible today. Just to the south of Dean Cross where we will cross Amber 1 we are again handed over, this time to the Scottish ATCC, Talla Sector controller who will look after us on the next leg of our flight. Our estimate for Talla is 09:23 and some little way before we get there we can expect to begin our descent. The cockpit work load is about to increase again and the frequencies and callsigns of our approach and landing aids are being checked. It is also an opportune moment to call the handling agent at Edinburgh to give details of the passenger load, fuel required, any engineering defects developed en-route and any of a dozen other things which will help speed the turn round if known about in advance. Also important at this time is a further cabin address, confirming our expected time of landing and the fact that we will shortly be reducing power for the descent. This wakes up any dozing passenger and warns any of a nervous disposition that the change in engine note is quite deliberate. It is also the signal for the cabin crew to go round and check that all seats are in the upright position and any loose articles safely stowed away. The crew meanwhile are going through their 'before descent' checklist. We will be making an approach under radar guidance for a landing using the ILS.

As we approach Talla we are cleared to descend to FL 90 initially

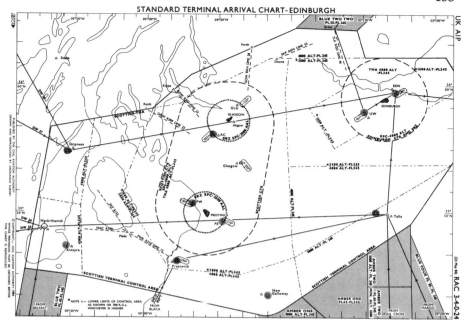

*Standard Terminal Arrival chart—Edinburgh.* (Reproduced by permission of the CAA.)

and to advise approaching that level. The power is slowly reduced and we begin to sink earthwards at a rate which is comfortable for the passengers. Traffic permitting the idea is to allow for a continuous descent all the way to final approach. As we come down towards FL 90 we are further cleared to FL 60 and handed over to the Approach Control Unit at Edinburgh for further descent and radar vectoring onto the extended centre line of the ILS. We now fly a series of headings as given to us by Approach Radar Controller until we are some eight miles from touchdown and just off the localiser beam. Our final radar heading will be one that allows us to 'cut' this beam at a shallow angle of about 30°, which allows for a positive indication on the ILS indicator and requires a reasonable rate of turn onto 'finals'.

In the cockpit there is also a landing check list to be done which includes switching on the 'Fasten Seat Belt' and 'No Smoking' signs in the passenger cabin. The cabin crew will check that all have complied and will report that all is ready. The undercarriage is selected down together with a small amount of flap and the landing lights are also switched on. The latter may seem odd especially in

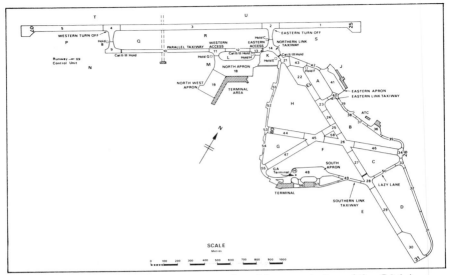

*Edinburgh—location of traffic blocks.* (Reproduced by permission of the CAA.)

broad daylight but it is done to make the aircraft more easily visible. The final approach is one of the most vulnerable phases of flight. With wheels and flaps down, power reduced, a relatively low airspeed and being close to the ground we are in no condition to carry out rapid evasive action so the more people who can see us the better.

The ILS localiser needle is hard to the right and the glide path needle is fully up as we approach the ILS beams. Gradually the localiser needle begins to move into the centre of the instrument and we establish the aircraft on the extended centre line. This done we fly level for a while until the glide path needle begins to move downwards towards the centre of the instrument. At this point we are fully established, centreline and glide path and report this over the R/T to the Approach Controller. Told to continue our approach we are put over to the Tower Controller and asked to report passing the outer marker. As soon as we call the tower we are given clearance to land together with a check on the surface wind speed and direction.

Through the windscreen we can see the approach lights beckoning us on and beyond them the runway lights. The ILS needles are firmly crossed in the middle of the instrument as we cross the threshold, reduce power, and touch down on the runway. Power all the way back and firmly but gently on go the brakes as we slow to our taxying speed. The Tower Controller tells us where to turn off the runway, the route to be followed and our parking area. As we taxy in the final check list is gone through which includes switching off the cabin warning signs, the landing lights, raising the flaps and shutting down any electrical systems no longer needed.

Stationary once more, with the engines stopped, the doors are opened and the steps come alongside to allow the passengers to disembark. The ground power unit appears on the apron and is coupled up to the aircraft, but then this is all beginning to sound familiar.

The flight just described is deliberately simple but will, hopefully, serve to demonstrate how the various pieces go together. The same principles apply even if our flight had taken us southward over Europe, westward over the Atlantic, or further west on into the Pacific. The aircraft would differ in size and shape but the navigational aids used would be remarkably similar, the accents heard in our earpieces would be strange but the airfields used would look not unfamiliar, even if we had never been there in our lives before. Air Traffic Control is about many things but it is always, always about people.

# Chapter 13

# *Towards the future*

History is strewn with the wreckage of forecasts and predictions of future requirements and events made by those who were bold, or foolish, enough to gaze into the crystal ball. The temptation to be dogmatic or over confident might well be tempered by remembering that it is not too far back in history that the most respected and learned of men were convinced that the earth was flat! What chance then, those who have the unenviable task of planning an ATC system for the future?

The development of the ATC system has been, and is always likely to be, evolutionary rather than revolutionary. In only a few short years man has progressed from a short hop to flight faster than sound and has even travelled to the moon. Within that period the history of ATC is even shorter but has also made great strides. At Kittyhawk a single frail flying machine lifted one man into the air. In 1983, London (Heathrow) airport saw the arrival and departure of 26.7 million passengers and Manchester 5.2 million. Add another 14.4 million at Gatwick, Stansted, Glasgow, Edinburgh, Prestwick and Aberdeen and the total becomes 45.3 million passengers. In addition 627,900 tonnes of cargo was moved in the United Kingdom alone, the world total must produce a figure quite beyond comprehension. It is reasonable to suppose that without the parallel development of the ATC system there would have been some pretty impressive figures for passengers killed and aircraft lost.

ATC is a customer orientated service and therefore tends to follow rather than lead. When the demand becomes apparent a way is found to deal with it. As a means of illustrating how changing demands come about it is interesting to look at the development of the civil airliner. There have been many manufacturers of civil aircraft but one company, Douglas, now McDonnell Douglas of the USA has been producing civil airliners for 40 years in an unbroken line. The figures quoted here are for the generic marks and may differ from those quoted elsewhere for specific developments of the type.

In 1933 there appeared the first of the line, the Douglas Commercial Number One or DC-1. The design of this aircraft was revolutionary at the time and although not immediately forseen was to herald the beginning of mass aerial transportation. Carrying 12 passengers at a speed of 180 mph only one example was built. Less than a year later the DC-2 was in production with a similar speed but with room for 14 passengers. This aircraft was to open up many of the internal routes in the USA, in Europe, and was to set many records. The following year, 1935, saw the introduction of the DC-3, an aircraft which was to do for air travel what steam did for land and sea travel. For the first time it was possible to operate a reliable and commercially viable air service at a cost that made flying popular. Eventually to be built in enormous numbers, for a while this type of aircraft carried fully 95 per cent of the world's civilian air traffic. A total of 455 DC-3s were built for airline use and a staggering 10,174 for military service. It saw service all over the world and became known by many names including Pionair (BEA), Dakota (RAF) and was also known to millions of US servicemen as the Skytrain, C-47, or 'Gooney Bird'. Carrying up to 36 passengers at 165 mph over 1,000 remain in service all over the world. The next design, the DC-5 was a departure from the low wing, twin engined layout of the DC-1 to 3. A high winged twin engined monoplane, it was to be overwhelmed by history as World War 2 brought about a demand for longer range aircraft and production ceased after only a few had been built.

The year 1942 saw the introduction of the longer range aircraft. A return to the low wing was made but this time with four engines. The DC-4 was able to carry 86 passengers at speeds of over 200 mph. This type made possible the introduction of routine trans-oceanic flights and became the mainstay of the US wartime long range transport fleet. Over 1,100 were built, many being converted for civilian use after the war to form, with the DC-3, the cornerstone of postwar civil aviation development. An advanced version of the DC-4, the DC-6, was to appear in 1946 with air conditioning, cabin pressurisation and room for up to 102 passengers travelling at 350 mph. In all 704 DC-6s were built. Advances in piston engine technology were to allow the introduction of the DC-7 in 1953. The first commercial aircraft with enough range to make transcontinental and trans-oceanic flights regardless of the prevailing winds, the Seven-Seas version had a range of 4,900 miles at 345 mph and a passenger capacity of 105.

The dawning of a new age was, however, just around the corner, pioneered by the beautiful De Havilland Comet which had first flown on July 27 1949. The era of the jet powered airliner had arrived and to enter the field Douglas introduced their DC-8. With low mounted swept wings and four pod-mounted jet engines the basic layout was very similar to that adopted by Boeing in their highly successful 707 series of aircraft. The DC-8 in its biggest version is 187 ft long and can carry 251 passengers non-stop for 6,700 miles at over 500 mph. As well as the need to develop a long range airliner there existed a requirement to replace many of the older and slower airliners used on the shorter routes. The DC-9, introduced in 1965 was the Douglas contender for a share of the lucrative market. The largest version of this aircraft carries 172 passengers over 1,000 miles at over 500 mph.

About this time a number of outside influences were to make their impact on civil aircraft design and, by association, with ATC methods. The cost of aviation fuel was rising steeply and to combat this the engine manufacturers were hard at work to develop quieter, more powerful, fuel efficient engines. Airports were reaching their capacity for handling traffic at the times of day dictated by public demand. Airport noise restrictions were being steadily introduced and the ATC service was running very close to maximum capacity at peak periods. The airlines themselves were considerably less tolerant of ATC imposed delays.

To help solve the problem of meeting increased demand against limited ATC and airport capacity, a partial answer came in the form of the 'Jumbo' airliner. More passengers carried in fewer aircraft would provide a breathing space for ATC, airports, and airlines finances alike. New engine technology allowed for the use of fewer engines and so the era of the tri-jet was born. The Douglas bid in this area came in the form of the DC-10, introduced in 1970. Carrying 380 passengers for 7,000 miles at a speed of 550 mph, the DC-10 and its counterparts have brought about a new age of jet travel. In service with 48 of the world's carriers the DC-10 serves 170 cities on six continents and carries more than 150,000 passengers every day.

For those whose duty it is to plan the future operations of the ATC system it is very difficult to forecast accurately where the major demand will be in say the next 10–15 years. Fortunately, from their standpoint, the enormous cost of developing completely new aircraft has slowed down the rate of change, allowing a breathing space for future needs to be identified and the means found to assimilate them into the existing system. It is also possible to identify a shift of emphasis of operations and to find ways of balancing that shift. Not too long ago the North Sea was somewhere where people went to catch fish. A few aircraft transitted the area to and from the Scandinavian countries, otherwise it was the almost exclusive domain of the military. And then along came the gas fields, followed by the discovery of oil. Now there is almost continuous helicopter activity to and from Aberdeen and the Scandinavian countries with the consequent increase in fixed wing traffic. Before this activity no airway existed north of the Forth/Clyde valley. It does now, together with a whole network of routes for use by helicopters as they service the gas and oil fields. The ability of the oil industry to find and recover oil in deeper water has turned their attention to the other side of the United Kingdom. How long before oil exploration rigs begin to appear off the Atlantic coastline to be followed by production platforms?

In spite of all the gloom cast by the financial world work on new projects is still going on. Contrary to all predictions the airship industry begins to look as though it might have a future. Even in the age of supersonic travel and space flight it could still have a role to play in the area of lifting heavy freight where time is not of the essence. Will the airship ever go into service and the ATC system have to find a way to accommodate it?

At this very moment a study is under way to investigate the possibility of space shuttles landing and taking off like ordinary aircraft. The horizontal take-off and landing concept has been around since man first left the ground in an aircraft but the take-off element is new in space flight. What influence will space travel have on the future operation of ATC?

Those who plan the future ATC service, what it will offer and what technical facilities it will need to make that possible have an unenviable task. It is tempting to gather all that is new in the technical field just for the sake of it. The question is does it do the job better or more efficiently than it is being done now? The manufacturing industry needs to sell its products but they must never be introduced simply because they are new.

The concept of ATC has changed little since its introduction. It exists primarily to avoid aircraft hitting each other and to achieve this aim in the most efficient manner possible. The practice of ATC, and indeed aviation as a whole, contains a large element of learning and it is from this learning that evolution springs. The adoption of radar for control purposes was the first giant leap forward and enabled the system to absorb the huge increase in growth that came about. This, however, created problems in its turn, such as the need to pass information quickly and accurately amongst the many who need to know.

The second giant leap forward came with the adoption of computer techniques and the ability to store and process vast quantities of information coupled with the ability to retrieve it quickly and distribute it at speed. Similarly, developments in the area of electronics have brought about major changes. The new generation of technical equipment both on the ground and in the air are themselves helping to rejuvenate the basic system although the problem of how best to interface all of the new facilities and techniques is likely to remain for some considerable time to come. Meanwhile, the system cannot be allowed to stagnate. Even the best maintained equipment wears out therefore a continuing programme of replacement and renewal is always under way.

Due to be commissioned in the near future are a number of new radar sites for ATC use. These are designed to give a better coverage from low to high level and to be technically compatible with the various types of processing equipment with which they are intended to interface. The location of these sites has been chosen carefully to give a generous overlap of coverage so that the system has an element of built-in redundancy in the event of loss of information from any one site.

Related changes are also taking place within the London Air Traffic Control Centre as part of the LATCC Development Plan, designed to bring together the best in current radar and computer technology. The control suites previously described are to be replaced by a new style of control suite known as Executive and

**Right** *CAA radar replacement programme—primary and secondary radar.* (Produced from information supplied by the CAA.)
*Great Dun Fell—Long range surveillance for LATCC*
*Claxby—Long range surveillance for LATCC*
*Debden—Approach Control (Stansted), long range surveillance and supplementary TMA surveillance for LATCC*
*Heathrow—Approach Control (Heathrow) and TMA surveillance for LATCC.*
*Pease Pottage—Approach Control (Gatwick) and TMA surveillance for LATCC.*

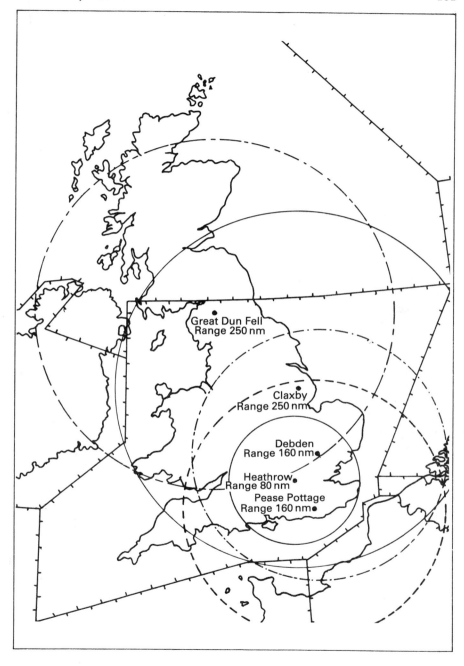

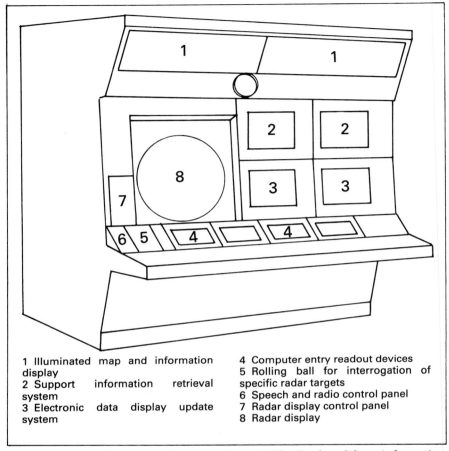

1 Illuminated map and information display
2 Support information retrieval system
3 Electronic data display update system
4 Computer entry readout devices
5 Rolling ball for interrogation of specific radar targets
6 Speech and radio control panel
7 Radar display control panel
8 Radar display

*A modern Air Traffic Control suite for use in an ATCC.* (Produced from information supplied by the CAA.)

Support or E&S. The 9020D computer system will provide a common data base for flight and radar data for both en-route and off route traffic. Each E&S suite will be manned by one Executive Controller (Radar) and one Support Controller. They will be of comparable grade and validation, the ability to do the same job permitting greater flexibility and interchangeability of staff. The Executive Controller will do the actual controlling of the traffic within his sector of operation. The Support Controller will be responsible for the major part of the computer input task and planning for the overall operation of the sector. He will also be responsible for the co-ordination with other sectors and air traffic service units as well as for telephone work. The use of the telephone will, however, be much reduced because of the ability to transfer data by other means. With a reduced sector staff it is expected that improved team work will be possible and the new system is also expected to significantly increase the traffic handling of each sector.

The Chief Sector Controller will no longer be positioned on the actual control suite. His job will be done by a Bank Supervisor who will be responsible for a number of sectors associated with a specific and defined geographical area. Each Chief Sector Controller will report in turn to the overall Watch Supervisor (Operations).

Concurrent with the bringing on line of the new radar sites and the E&S suites is a major change in the processing and distribution of flight data. That historical cornerstone of ATC, the flight progress strip, will be phased out to be replaced by a data display system known as EDDUS or, Electronic Data Display and Update System. Each E&S suite will be equipped with one or more data displays and their associated input devices so that the information displayed can be altered via the computer to reflect the current situation.

The development of the ATC system on a national basis can be undertaken given the technical ability and the necessary finance. What is infinitely more difficult is to do the same on an international basis. There are countries which lie along international air routes whose technical ability and means to provide finance are severely limited. International help is not always welcomed either as they remain countries and nations in their own right and will not easily give up control of their sovereign airspace to others. There is a problem then with the highly industrialised nations creating very efficient ATC systems which are way above that provided down the line. There is little point in being able to generate vast quantities of traffic if it only causes embarrassment and confusion at an FIR boundary.

Another area of ATC development currently being investigated and using computer technology concerns the introduction of an automatic method of conflict prediction. With flight plan data being stored in the computer data bank it is possible to project ahead the flight paths of aircraft being controlled and to predict those that will lead to conflict. It is also possible to ask the computer to investigate the possible options and to discard those which will lead to further conflict. Having examined the options the possible courses of action can then be displayed. There is no doubt that this system has a value but it is limited in that the examination is done in the static mode whereas the aircraft are always in the dynamic mode.

An alternative method, also under investigation, is for the conflict prediction information to be presented in the aircraft itself for subsequent reaction by the crew. In addition to supplying the required information to ATC via the SSR and the aircraft mounted transponder it is technically possible for individual transponders to listen to each other. By this means it is possible for them to become aware of another approaching transponder and warn the crew that another aircraft is encroaching on their airspace. One or both crews could then initiate avoiding action. The difficulties of this system are twofold. The resolving of one conflict may lead straight into another and potentially more dangerous one and the system could easily become overloaded or confused in areas of high activity such as a TMA. It also has the effect of splitting the executive control function, even if only momentarily, and this at a time when a co-ordinated reaction is most needed.

It is but a short step to think of a fully automated ATC system with both the ATC function and the aircraft being under the control of inter-linked computers, with every flight slotted into a pre-ordained pattern. Such a system would run at maximum efficiency all of the time—or would it?

Some far reaching and large assumptions are being made here. Is it really possible that every aircraft will be ready on time, that no coach bringing passengers to the airport will ever break down or be stuck in a traffic jam? What of the passengers themselves? To make absolutely certain of meeting a take-off time they would have to reach the airport and be processed well ahead of time and this is not likely to be acceptable to the majority. Such a system would require a large element of technical redundancy because it must never, ever, fail. Nothing must ever go wrong—go wrong—go wrong—go wrong! Should it happen and a disaster result it is also important that someone can be identified as being the responsible person.

There is a high probability that the practice and art of aviation and Air Traffic Control will always employ a large and essential element of human intervention. Meanwhile the present ATC system continues, day in and day out, year in and year out, to meet the demands placed upon it. It is there to provide a service and to ensure a safe, orderly and expeditious flow of air traffic. Its existence and efficiency depends not only upon the technical wonders of a modern age but to a large extent on the men and women who work within it and their ability to maintain a high standard of efficiency as well as a justifiable pride in their own efforts. There is also a measure of comfort for those who remain firmly earthbound. The aircraft producing the contrail high over their heads or that can be heard but not seen on the worst winter's day, is under control, guided by unseen radio navigational aids and controlled by unheard voices. Aids and voices that continue long after decent law abiding citizens are in bed.

Clipper one niner tree, turn right heading zero niner two.

Speedbird five tree seven is over Daventry at this time.

Blackbox two two is level at flight level four five zero.

Harpoon tree one and four two ready for take-off.

Lufthansa two zero eight changing to Amsterdam—thank you, sir, and good day.

# Glossary

**AFTN** Aeronautical Fixed Telecommunications Network.
**AIP** Aeronautical Information Publication.
**AIS** Aeronautical Information Service.
**amsl** Above Mean Sea Level.
**ASMI** Airfield Surface Movement Indicator.
**ATC** Air Traffic Control.
**ATCA** Air Traffic Control Assistant.
**ATCC** Air Traffic Control Centre.
**ATCEU** Air Traffic Control Evaluation Unit.
**ATCO** Air Traffic Control Officer.
**ATIS** Automated Terminal Information Service.
**ATSU** Air Traffic Service Unit.
**ATZ** Aerodrome Traffic Zone.
**AUS** Airspace Utilisation Section.

**CAA** Civil Aviation Authority.
**CAAFU** Civil Aviation Authority Flying Unit.
**CATC** College of Air Traffic Control.
**CAVOK** Ceiling and Visibility—OK.
**CTE** College of Telecommunications Engineering.
**CZ** Control Zone.

**D&D** Distress and Diversion.
**DFTI** Distance From Touchdown Indicator.
**DME** Distance Measuring Equipment.
**DVOR** Doppler Very High Frequency Omni-directional Range.

**E&S** Executive and Support.

**FDPS** Flightplan Data Processing System.
**FIR** Flight Information Region.
**FIS** Flight Information Service.
**FL** Flight Level.

**GCA** Ground Controlled Approach.
**GMC** Ground Movement Control.
**GMT** Greenwich Mean Time.

**HF** High Frequency.

**ICAO** International Civil Aviation Organisation.
**IFF** Identification—Friend or Foe.
**IFR** Instrument Flight Rules.
**ILS** Instrument Landing System.
**IMC** Instrument Meteorological Conditions.
**IRVR** Instrumented Runway Visual Range.

**JAS** Joint Airmiss Section.
**JATCRU** Joint Air Traffic Control Radar Unit.

**LARS** Lower Airspace Radar Service.
**LF** Low Frequency.

**MF** Medium Frequency.
**MLS** Micro Wave Landing System.
**MRSA** Mandatory Radar Service Area.
**MTI** Moving Target Indicator.

**NATS** National Air Traffic Services.
**NDB** Non-directional Beacon.
**NOTAM** Notice to Airmen.

**OACC** Oceanic Air Traffic Control Centre.

**PAPI** Precision Approach Path Indicator.
**PE** Permanent Echo.
**PRDS** Processed Radar Display System.

**Q-CODE** Coded Wireless Telegraphy Messages.
**QFE** Barometric Pressure at Aerodrome Level.
**QNH** Barometric Pressure at Sea Level.

**RADAR** Radio Detection and Ranging.
**ROP** Runway Observation Post.
**RT** Radio Telephone.
**RVR** Runway Visual Range.

**ScATCC** Scottish Air Traffic Control Centre.
**SHF** Super High Frequency.
**SID** Standard Instrument Departure.
**SIGMET** Significant Meteorological Information.
**SRA** Surveillance Radar Approach.
**SRZ** Special Rules Zone.
**SSR** Secondary Surveillance Radar.
**STOL** Short Take-off and Landing.
**SVFR** Special Visual Flight Rules.

**TEE** Telecommunications Engineering Establishment.
**TMA** Terminal Control Area.
**TRSB** Time Reference Scanning Beam.

**UAR** Upper Air Route.
**UAS** Upper Air Space.
**UHF** Ultra High Frequency.

**VASI** Visual Approach Slope Indicator.
**VFR** Visual Flight Rules.
**VHF** Very High Frequency.
**VLF** Very Low Frequency.
**VMC** Visual Meteorological Conditions.
**VOLMET** Continuous Broadcast of Meteorological Information.
**VOR** Very High Frequency Omni-directional Radio Range.

**WT** Wireless Telegraphy.

**ZULU** Time Based on Greenwich Mean Time.

# *Appendices*

## 1 Frequency Banding

| | | |
|---|---|---|
| **VLF** | Very High Frequency | Below 30 kHz |
| **LF** | Low Frequency | 30–300 kHz |
| **MF** | Medium Frequency | 300–3,000 kHz |
| **HF** | High Frequency | 3–30 mHz |
| **VHF** | Very High Frequency | 30–300 mHz |
| **UHF** | Ultra High Frequency | 300–3,000 mHz |
| **SHF** | Super High Frequency | 3,000–30,000 mHz |

## 2 Frequency Spectrum

| | | |
|---|---|---|
| 30–300 Hz | | Domestic power supplies |
| 3 kHz–30 kHz | **VLF** | Very long range W/T (Rugby Radio) |
| 30 kHz–300 kHz | **LF** | Decca |
| 300 kHz–3,000 kHz | **MF** | Consol, Loran, Non-directional beacons |
| 3,000 kHz–30,000 kHz | **HF** | W/T and R/T |
| 30,000 kHz–300 mHz | **VHF** | VHF R/T VOR ILS (Localiser) |
| 300 mHz–3,000 mHz | **UHF** | 'L' band radar, DME, SSR, ILS (Glidepath) |
| 3,000 mHz–30,000 mHz | **SHF** | 'S, X, and Q' band radars (ASMI) |

## 3 Further examples of ICAO designators for aircraft types

| | | | |
|---|---|---|---|
| **CONC** | BAC Concorde | **A300** | Airbus |
| **S210** | Sud Est Caravelle | **AN24** | Antonov 24 |

| | | | |
|---|---|---|---|
| AT98 | Carvair | C120 | Cessna 120 |
| BE55 | Beech 55 | C152 | Cessna Aerobat |
| BE90 | Beech King Air 90 | C337 | Cessna Skymaster |
| E110 | Bandeirante | DH6 | De Havilland Twin |
| BN2 | Islander | | Otter |
| AC60 | Grand Commander | DH7 | De Havilland Dash 7 |
| BA11 | BAC One-Eleven | FK27 | Friendship |
| BA46 | BAC 146 | FK28 | Fellowship |
| HS25 | HS125 | HP7 | Herald |
| BH06 | Bell Jet Ranger | CV99 | Coronado 990 |
| B707 | Boeing 707–200 | PARO | Cherokee Arrow |
| B72S | Boeing 720B | PA23 | Aztec |
| AC6T | Turbo Commander | PA28 | Cherokee |
| LR28 | Learjet 28 | PA30 | Twin Comanche |
| LR55 | Learjet 55 | PA31 | Navajo |
| IL76 | Ilyushin IL-76 | SH5 | Belfast |
| C130 | Hercules | SH7 | Skyvan |
| L101 | L1011 Tristar | TU34 | Tupolev 134 |
| DC10 | Douglas DC10 | TU54 | Tupolev 154 |
| DC86 | Super DC8 | SC3 | Bulldog |
| N265 | Sabreliner | VC8 | Viscount 800 |
| B737 | Boeing 737 | VC9 | Vanguard/ |
| B767 | Boeing 767 | | Merchantman |
| HST3 | Trident 3 | WA12 | Jodel D120 |

# 4 Further examples of ICAO designators and call-signs for aircraft operating agencies

| | | |
|---|---|---|
| Aer Lingus Teoranta | EI | Aer Lingus |
| Air Atlantique | DG | Atlantic |
| Air Canada | AC | Air Canada |
| Air Ecosse Ltd | WG | Ecosse Air |
| Air Europe | AE | Air Europe |
| Air France | AF | Airfrans |
| Air UK Ltd | UK | Ukay |
| Alitalia | AZ | Alitalia |
| All Nipon Airways | NH | All Nipon |
| American Airlines | AA | Flagship |
| Britannia Airways Ltd | BY | Britannia |
| British Airways | BA | Speedbird |
| British Airtours Ltd | KT | Beatours |

| British Caledonian Airways | BR | Caledonian |
|---|---|---|
| British Midland Airways | BD | Midland |
| Canadian Pacific Airlines | CP | Empress |
| Dan Air | DA | Danair |
| Flying Tiger Line | FT | Tiger |
| Japan Airlines Co | JL | Japanair |
| Middle East Airlines | ME | Cedar Jet |
| Pan American World Airways | PA | Clipper |
| Romanian Air Transport | RO | Tarom |
| Sabena | SN | Sabena |
| Scandinavian Airlines System | SK | Scandinavian |
| Trans-World Airlines | TW | TWA |
| United Air Services | UA | United |
| Wardair Canada Ltd | WD | Wardair |
| World Airways Inc | WO | World Airways |

# 5 Further examples of ICAO four letter location indicators

## Foreign airports

| AAAD | Adelaide | EHRD | Rotterdam |
|---|---|---|---|
| ABBN | Brisbane | EICK | Cork |
| ACXM | Christmas Island | EINN | Shannon |
| ADDM | Munich | ELLX | Luxembourg |
| ADDN | Darwin | ENFB | Oslo |
| ASAS | Alice Springs | EPWA | Warsaw |
| ASCA | Canberra | FACT | Cape Town |
| ATDN | Dresden | GCXO | Tenerife |
| BIKF | Keflavik | HECA | Cairo |
| CYHB | Hudson Bay | HEPS | Port Said |
| CYHZ | Halifax | KBOS | Boston |
| CYOW | Ottawa | KDAL | Dallas |
| CYQB | Quebec | KDET | Detroit |
| CYQX | Gander | KLAX | Los Angeles |
| CYUL | Montreal | KMIA | Miami |
| DNKN | Kano | KORD | Chicago |
| DNMM | Lagos | LCNC | Nicosia |
| EBOS | Ostend | LEAL | Alicante |
| EDBB | Berlin | LEBL | Barcelona |
| EDDH | Hamburg | LEIB | Ibiza |
| EDDK | Cologne | LFBD | Bordeaux |
| EHEH | Eindhoven | LFLY | Lyons |

| | | | |
|---|---|---|---|
| **LFPG** | Paris (Charles de Gaulle) | **NZAA** | Auckland |
| | | **NZWN** | Wellington |
| **LIML** | Milan | **OLBA** | Beirut |
| **LIRF** | Rome | **OPKC** | Karachi |
| **LLBG** | Tel-Aviv | **RJAA** | Tokyo |
| **LMML** | Malta | **RPMM** | Manila |
| **LPPT** | Lisbon | **VABB** | Bombay |
| **LSGG** | Geneva | **VHHH** | Hong Kong |
| **LYDU** | Dubrovnik | | |

## British airports

| | | | |
|---|---|---|---|
| **EGBB** | Birmingham | **EGNV** | Tees-side |
| **EGDM** | Boscombe Down | **EGNX** | East Midlands |
| **EGGD** | Bristol | **EGPB** | Sumburgh |
| **EGGP** | Liverpool | **EGPD** | Aberdeen |
| **EGGW** | Luton | **EGPF** | Glasgow |
| **EGHI** | Southampton | **EGPK** | Prestwick |
| **EGMC** | Southend | **EGSS** | Stansted |
| **EGNH** | Blackpool | **EGTE** | Exeter |
| **EGNT** | Newcastle | **EGTK** | Oxford |

# 6   Some commonly used flight progress strip markings

/      After passing (flight level or reporting point).

T      Aircraft given time check.

Q̧      Aircraft given appropriate altimeter setting.

H      Aircraft instructed to hold.

↑      Climb.

R̂      Climb when instructed by radar.

⟹   Joining flight (controlled airspace).

⟋⟍   Leaving controlled airspace.

✝✝►   Maintain (flight level).

R/V  Radar vectoring for a visual approach.

R/I  Radar vectoring for an ILS approach.


# 7 Transition altitude and level

## Transition altitude

Transition altitude is the altitude at or below which the vertical position of an aircraft is normally controlled by reference to altitude. Wherever possible there is a common transition altitude where there are a number of airfields within a Control Zone. The transition altitude for civil aerodromes situated outside controlled airspace is normally 3,000 ft.

## Transition level

The transition level is the lowest flight level available for use above the transition altitude. It is determined by reference to the table below.

a) Within controlled airspace by the controlling authority, normally based upon the QNH of the major aerodrome where more than one is involved.

b) Outside controlled airspace by the aerodrome authority, based upon aerodrome QNH.

## Transition layer

The transition layer is the airspace between the transition altitude and the transition level.

# Table for determining the transition level

| Aerodrome QNH in millibars | Transition altitude (ft) | | | |
|---|---|---|---|---|
| | **3,000** | **4,000** | **5,000** | **6,000** |
| 1050–1032 | 25 | 35 | 45 | 55 |
| 1031–1014 | 30 | 40 | 50 | 60 |
| 1013–996 | 35 | 45 | 55 | 65 |
| 995–978 | 40 | 50 | 60 | 70 |
| 977–960 | 45 | 55 | 65 | 75 |
| 959–943 | 50 | 60 | 70 | 80 |

# Index